GROWING UP TO LOVE, SEX AND MARRIAGE

GROWING UP TO LOVE, SEX AND MARRIAGE

BY

SIDNEY L. SANDS, M.D.

THE CHRISTOPHER PUBLISHING HOUSE
BOSTON, U.S.A.

TO

GOLDA

CONTENTS

INTRODUCTION

The purpose of this book is to offer a "philosophy of marriage" predicated on the belief that the contributions of the biological and social sciences to our understanding of the nature of the human organism can provide us with definite guides to a fuller realization of our own best potentials. It is the author's studied conviction that love and sex are the most powerful forces for good inherent in man and that the institution of marriage represents the best agency for the fullest expression thereof.

That marriages fail is less an indictment of the institution than it is of people. People fail, not marriages, and failure can generally be traced to the *immaturity* of one or both partners. Therefore, the function of a philosophy of marriage must, if it is to be meaningful and useful, aid the individual in the attainment of maturity. To do this, it must show us what we can become — establish a model of self that we would aspire to be, *but one which can be logically constructed from the knowledge of what we are.* This can best be done by utilizing hard-won empirical data from such diverse fields as biology, psychology, anthropology and sociology, to achieve a synthesis enabling us to see with new clarity the meaning of love, sex and marriage in human life. Knowledge of what we are and have been, as a specie and as individuals, can then be utilized to indicate what we are capable of becoming. If we can learn, we can change, and *what* we learn can influence the quality and quantity of that change. We have to know where we have been if we are to have any idea of where we are going, and we must know our own potentials if we are to have any goals toward which we may hopefully labor.

This, then will be not so much a book about "Problems," but about human growth and development and the nature of maturity and the maturation process, all keyed to the central task of giving us the means of being better husbands, wives and parents. If to do this, we must base our philosophy and our models on the bedrock of the biological and social sciences, this does not preclude the possibility for a way of life consistent with cherished ethico-religious ideals. It is precisely our objective to give new meaning and substance to those very ideals which have too often suffered when blind faith or fear, ignorance and superstition have been their sole support.

It is time that we dare to be better than we are, but we can only do so if, from knowing what we are, we may logically define what we may yet become. To that end is this book hopefully and with all humility submitted.

One may legitimately ask, "Why such a book at this time?" My answer to that is, that in spite of all we have learned about Man and Mankind, we have not moved far from our primitive ancestors emotionally and have, in fact, created conditions which threaten the whole fabric of human history. For all our knowledge, more and more people appear to be less and less capable of adjusting with any consistent faith and satisfaction to the life they are leading. Nowhere is this more pathetically demonstrated than in the statistics of our Divorce Courts, Juvenile Courts, and the case-records of those dealing with disturbed children and adults. It is a sad commentary on the human race, that for all our technical achievements and our so-called high standard of living, we have such great difficulty living with each other at any level of social organization. If men and women cannot communicate and adjust effectively to each other, it is little wonder that tensions exist which divide and endanger larger social groups, be they racial, religious or national in their composition. Present day society, even in this blessed land, can take little pride in the record of its own vital statistics.

For the purpose of this book, it is necessary that we identify some of the signs and symptoms of our social disorder and in broad perspective see these in the light of biological as well as social history. With this behind us, we may then proceed to the study of human growth and development in terms which will enable us better to see our own potentials and what it means to "grow up" to love, sex and marriage.

Growing Up to Love, Sex and Marriage

CHAPTER I

On Man and Society

1. *The Basic Conflicts*

Biology is, by definition, the study of life. More accurately, it is the study of phenomena associated with what we now arbitrarily call "living" matter. Such study embraces an ever-enlarging domain whose boundaries merge with those of both the physical and social sciences. Individual biologists may be investigating such diverse problems as the metabolism of single-celled organisms or the social behavior of groups of organisms. The study of man obviously can involve considerations not ordinarily within the confines of biology, but no understanding of human life can be complete if we disregard those specific biologic attributes which we share with all living things. For the student of "life," the history of man is but a special part of a longer story, whose beginnings are but dimly perceived and whose final chapter no one will ever read. From research in the many fields of science, we are slowly piecing together the nature of the complex patterns of evolving life-forms and processes as they have developed in the enormous framework of time and space. Man is but a late-comer on the scene. His recorded history is but a few brief hours on the biological clock, yet in these scant moments, his achievements and his works are indeed fantastic. After millions of years of the existence of other forms of life on earth, man suddenly emerged as a distinct specie and within a few thousand years, achieved what appears to be the dominant position in the dynamic we loosely call "life." But, lest we grow too worshipful of our own image, let us note with grave regard one solitary fact: man, the organism, has achieved what no other living creature could ever accomplish and that is the capacity to destroy himself and all living things of the earth. That the means have been discovered is not nearly so terrifying as is the simple fact that no other form of life has ever shown such a ferocious capacity for attacking and destroying large masses of its own specie. Man's creative ability has enabled him to invent such crimes against himself and his own kind as to spread terror and confusion among all the peoples who crowd this tiny planet. Hate, fear, suspicion and jealousy flourish like flowers of evil to divide nations, groups, creeds and, most piteously of all, man and woman.

If we make record of this aspect of man's character, we must also give recognition to a more ennobling virtue. No other living creature has labored so hard or so desperately to preserve life. Against great odds, he has fought against the ravages of disease and famine, helped the needy and oppressed and prayed to his various Gods for the salvation of all mankind. He has enshrined the scholars and artists who have given us wisdom and beauty and he has revered the statesmen who have fought the good fight for a better world.

Thus, man the creator and man the destroyer constitute a paradox of monumental proportions, and never has the conflict been more fatefully nor frighteningly joined than in these days of our years wherein we possess the means of completely wiping from the face of the earth every last vestige of life as we know it.

A further complication to human adjustment stems from those differences in form and biological function which distinguish male and female. Thus, we must struggle not only with the universal conflict (love vs. hate, creativity vs. destructiveness), in all humans, but also that arising from the biological difference which divides the specie into two quite distinctly different beings. In ancient times, these particular biological differentiations determined quite easily the social roles of each. Relatively simple conventions governed the status and functions of the male and the female in the family group and in the tribe. This is still partly true today, but sex-determined biological roles no longer clearly define social roles and we are witnessing in more recent times what we somewhat facetiously call the battle-of-the-sexes. Feminine protest against real or imagined injustices in "the man's world" has been voiced for what has been too loosely referred to as equality. There are those who sincerely believe that women may have lost much more than they have gained; that in their striving for more independence, they have come to derogate their biological and domestic role, inhibit their deepest sexual feelings and end up either as "masculinized" career girls or as neurotic wives. Of equal importance is the effect on men who, moved by some sense of justice, have granted or yielded many of the rights sought by women, and now find themselves competing with women and feeling threatened with emasculation. This, in turn, inevitably gives rise to both deliberate and quite unconscious rebellion in men against the seeming threat of domination by the female. This subject has been given extensive treatment by others and the interested reader is referred to some representative works in the appended bibliography. For our present purposes, there is no point in elaborating on this theme nor in debating the moral issues involved. Suffice it to say that here is yet another paradox of human life. For all our achievements, we are racked by this second conflict which threatens the roles we play as men and women. Nowhere in nature can we find any other organism so desperately struggling with such pervasive urges to create and destroy their own kind, and in no other specie do we witness so much protest against their biological and social roles.

2. Modern Times

With these two basic conflicts in mind, we begin to sense something of the tragic in human existence; of what in western civilization made possible the dire prophecies and polemics of Nietzche, Schopenhauer, Wagner, Spengler, Henry Adams and others. An examination of some aspects of life in contemporary America is hardly reassuring.

We in America have created a mythical morality, sexual and otherwise. We have laid claim to a monopoly on virtue in our personal, public and political conduct. We look with scorn on the modes and customs of people in other lands and smugly set ourselves apart as being not only different, but better than they. The fact is, we are a nation of moral hypocrites — not because we are worse than any other nation, but because we tell ourselves we are better. We loudly proclaim (as much for ourselves as anyone else) that we are the most honest, the most Godfearing, the most democratic, the cleanest and the most virtuous nation on earth. We pride ourselves on having outgrown the residual burdens of puritanism and certain restrictive attitudes of religious fundamentalism, but we have failed to leaven our factual knowledge and new attitudes with wisdom in the use thereof. Despite our public proclamation of holiness and our portrayal of the ideal male and female as the eternal Boy Scout and his mother, we betray ourselves daily in thousands of ways; in the padded expense accounts; in our income-tax returns; in our violations of traffic laws; in our "restricted" neighborhoods, clubs and schools; in our gambling, drinking and use of narcotics; in our "big-time" athletics; and in the many ways we deceive ourselves and others with big or little lies.

We want our children to have wholesome desires and intelligent controls, but we set them rather horrible examples in our conduct of family life and in the world we offer them. We turn them over to others to educate, insist on the "best" for them and refuse to provide the means; making the teacher's task so demanding and unrewarding that only the most noble or most inept will seek their careers in that profession. The mass media pour a constant barrage of pictures, stories and sounds of crime, violence and licentiousness on our eyes and ears and escape the censor by tacking on rather specious endings to the stories. It is the crime that sells the magazine or the movie. It is not the triumph of virtue which sells the story or fills the theater, but the opportunity afforded the spectator to share vicariously the experiences of those over whom virtue will, for reasons often not clearly nor artfully presented, in fact triumph.   Worse even than this are the efforts of the advertising people to sell "the product."   The public is urged to face "the truth;" meaning, see this picture, it's hot stuff!   Or, read this exposé of Hollywood; meaning, here's a juicy bit of scandal.   Look at the magazine racks at any large newsstand or store.   Prominently displayed are the biggest expanses of bosom ever exposed to so many ogling eyes.   Month after month, the same bosoms and various other portions of female anatomy reappear, to be bought and drooled over by an amazing swarm of "art-lovers."   For most people, sex has become fixed in one big dirty joke, never to be entirely cleansed of the pornographic image, the indecent gesture or the guilt-laden loveless lust of misguided adolescence.

Another clue to our national character is revealed in many movies, TV programs, comic strips and jokes. This is our stereotyped husband and wife.   He is usually depicted as a fumbling dolt forever struggling to cope with his cleverer, domineering wife and their fiendishly precocious offspring.   He is the eternal fall-guy caught between the millstones of job and home. His boss is usually seen as a hot-tempered, ulcer-ridden head-hunter.   His wife is depicted as an overgrown Girl Scout, complete with bosom, biceps and brain. Only the latter are ever operational and that for the purpose of showing up the inadequacies of her spouse. Between them, the boss and the wife wring from our "hero" every shred of dignity and self-esteem he might possibly hope to have.   However overdrawn this portrait might be, it is not without its basis in fact. It is this image of himself that the American male is forever fighting to disprove. In "The Secret Life of Walter Mitty" by James Thurber, we find the essence of such a man. Think of him with a perpetual erection, desperately trying to prove and maintain his masculinity, and the picture becomes pathetically complete. In actual life, the wife is herself in constant conflict regarding her femininity, unsure of her actual status, alarmed by her reactions to the tasks of the homemaker, confused by her ineffective controls over her mate and children, and too often frustrated by her sex role, she cultivates the outward manifestations of femininity and inwardly resents, regrets and despairs of her past, present and future as a woman.

The effects of all this are responded to by the manufacturers and hucksters who exploit every human dissatisfaction and need; and in fact so exaggerate it as to mesmerize a large segment of the population into the belief that there must be no pain, no worry, no jangled nerves, no upset stomach and no sleepless nights. Success, beauty and tranquillity are available to all, in creams, powders, pills, liquids, or in the right gadgets, be they brassieres, automatic washers, or automobiles with super hydro-flex transubstantiators. Everybody is expected to have complexes and frustrations, *but* the real sin is not to buy the bright promise of relief that the ads offer.

All these things are pointed up to indicate the confusing and chaotic atmosphere in which our children must grow and find their way. It is in this bewildering jet-propelled flux of experiences that they begin to ask the important questions and soon discover that what

is preached, is rarely practiced and too often is so
badly presented as to arouse suspicion as to its intrinsic
merit and its applicability.   Parents, however badly
they adjust to each other or to life, are nevertheless
concerned about their children and in many cases are
frankly alarmed at the attitudes and values of their
offspring.   Junior and his dad are not really pals and
Mary does not bring her confidences to mother.   Junior
and Mary appear insatiable in their demands for
privileges and often lie and cheat to satisfy their own
desires.   When caught, they are either defiant or they
smugly blame it all on the folks.   In the area of sexual
behavior, parents are shocked by what they hear and
read, but feel powerless to cope with the problem of
effective communication.   Beyond having a few frank
talks about the mechanics of sex, they are impotent to
make meaningful the standards they profess to believe
in.

Premarital sexual relations, not only for men, but for
women, are not exclusively products of the post-war
period.   However, much as we may wish to believe
that "nice girls from good homes" never get into such
relationships, and certainly never did in "my day," the
facts contradict this.   That this is now happening more
often than it did twenty to forty years ago may be
true, but there is evidence that when in the past this
took place, it did so under somewhat different circumstances and often for different reasons than are largely
current today.   In those earlier times, it tended to occur
between engaged couples unable to wait until the
marriage vows had been exchanged.   In this instance,
the young girl often gave up her chastity under pressure from the male and her own unacknowledged de-

sires; an action which, though it occurred between the betrothed, was too often paid for with excessive guilt and unconscious resentment within the girl. More frequently than not, this sexual relationship occurred under less than desirable circumstances and was far from satisfying to either partner, but especially for the female. Thus, coupled with the associated negative emotions (guilt and resentment), it set the stage for later troubles. The honeymoon was robbed of much of its significance and the ground was prepared for many bitter moments to come. We must recognize that these painful emotions derived from more than mere disappointment in the sexual experience itself. Popular and conventional attitudes regarding sex were such as to burden most young people with ignorance, guilt and fear. The sense of "sin" was very real and sex, even in marriage, was pervaded with this notion. When, in this atmosphere, relations occurred before marriage, it was inevitable that the reactions would often be extreme. Since the male, too, was affected, even if to a lesser degree, by these socio-religious attitudes, his own subsequent behavior was reflected in the marriage. Guilty in his own mind and disappointed in both himself and his partner, he tended to abandon the romantic role and, once the marriage was officially instituted, reduced sex to a hasty, fumbling, quasi-rape which ignored the sensitivities and needs of his wife and left them both confused, hurt and deeply troubled. Guilt and ignorance caused the wife to accept with further resentment her sexual "duty" and seek her rewards and satisfactions in her children. The husband, frustrated by his own failings and his wife's frigidity often sought satisfaction elsewhere, in a rather desperate pursuit of his lost manhood. In such an atmosphere, it is little wonder that the ordinary stresses and strains of family life became magnified. Looking back upon the scene in the 1920's, with these conditions in mind, we see the adults of the "jazz age" as rather shocking caricatures of God's handiwork. The legacy of that period has left its taint upon the succeeding generations and revealed a decadence frightening to behold behind its mask of chromeplated virtue. With the economic boom and bust, and with the growing awareness of the "new look" in psychology due to Freud's theories of sex and personality, the excesses of that period begin to become meaningful. Today's parents are the direct descendants of those times. With the coming of World War II, tremendous pressures, problems and temptations found a generation of vulnerable young people who are now parents; a bit dazed by life and completely baffled by their own children who are the present younger generation.

In this brief introduction, we have seen man, a latecomer on the vast stage of life, emerging as the dominant specie over all living things, yet torn by terrible conflicts which threaten his biological role, and beyond that, his very existence. We have seen that despite his awesome achievements, he has and is doing a bad job of adjusting to himself and his fellow-creatures, as manifested by his recent past and present way of life. He may well be now at a critical point in his history. Yet despite the gloomy overtones of this thesis, the author numbers himself among those who believe that there is hope for mankind and find in man's potential for mature love the basis for such hope. It will therefore be the task of this book to develop from the facts and theories of the biological and social sciences a dynamic picture of life as it can be from birth to death; presenting a concept of maturity which may enable us to utilize the forces of love and sex in the institution of marriage for the greater happiness of ourselves and those who shall walk beside us.

CHAPTER II

THE HUMAN ORGANISM

1. *Introduction to the Subject*

The study of human *behavior,* as contrasted perhaps with the study of human anatomy and physiology, has always been heavily colored and influenced by the prevailing religious and cultural attitudes of the time. Behavior was, in the past, evaluated as good or bad, right or wrong according to moral, esthetic or religious concepts held by local authorities (church or secular) and supported by popular opinion, rather than as an outgrowth of empirical study. Such terms as Will, Soul, Constitution and others were freely used and were given quite definite meaning without any regard for experimental validation. What man *ought* to be was of greater concern than what man *is,* and if at times this produced noble and profound statements about man, it also restricted the scope of study and impaired the progress of free inquiry into the vexing problems of cosmology and psychology. The gradual development of scientific method in the physical and biological sciences was inevitably followed by its application to psychology and the social sciences. The inquisitive mind of man pushed through the restraining walls of speculative philosophy and institutionalized religion and sought to understand human behavior through objective, systematic study and experimentation. The evolutionary nature of life processes and forms, and even of knowledge itself, became recognized and accepted over the protests of mystics and theologians who held quite contrary views. Slowly, and at times painfully, solid advances have been made which contribute to a continuously enlarging understanding of human behavior. It is from this source that I wish to borrow, in the attempt to establish the foundations for a way of thinking about love, sex and marriage; a way that however much it may be grounded in biology and psychology need not in any way detract from our highest aspirations and spiritual values.

2. *Intra-uterine Life and the Trauma of Birth*

The process of fertilization, uniting not only the sexual partners, but more specifically the male sperm cell and the female ovum, brings into being the living human organism. Although at that moment it bears no resemblance to man, woman or child, it nevertheless is the repository for the genetic potentials of a very specific and unique individual; unquestionably human, but distinct from all other humans. Furthermore, from the time of conception it is an "experiencing" organism. The kinds of experiences it has during the period of gestation are important for us to understand and must be seen as a significant part of the total life history. Over a period of approximately nine months, the tiny cell grows, multiplies, alters its shape and slowly evolves into the familiar form we see at birth. During this period, it lives in a fluid medium, in an atmosphere of total darkness and relatively constant temperature and pressure. Its metabolic needs are met automatically through the responses of the mother's body to chemical changes in the baby. Oxygen and food-stuff is supplied through the mother's blood stream which is linked to that of the baby, and, in reverse, the waste products are drained off, to be eliminated via the excretory organs of the mother. In short, there is a minimum of external stimulation applied to the organism and almost immediate satisfaction of all its needs. It is as close to an ideal situation as can be conceived of in psychobiologic terms.

During the latter days of pregnancy the size and special chemistry of the baby, plus progressive changes in the hormonal status of the mother, render the uterus increasingly more irritable until at last it begins to contract rhythmically and vigorously to empty itself of its burden. It is these contractions of the uterus which announce the onset of labor and the birth process. It also initiates a whole new order of experiences for the organism. The forceful labor efforts squeeze the baby into the birth-canal, restrict its random or reflex movements, impede its oxygen supply (and carbon dioxide loss), applying moulding pressures to its head and in so doing stimulate the organism to such a degree that a complex chain of physical-chemical responses are invoked which form the primitive model for what we later experience and recognize as fear or anxiety. Under such stress is the infant born, but emergence from the body of the mother by no means relieves the baby of all distressing stimulations. The separation from the mother and the radically different environmental conditions which now prevail makes necessary the use of new modes of adjustment and the acquisition of increasingly complex skills. He is now in the world of noise, lights, sudden changes in temperature, rapid shifts in his position in space, irregular pressures on different parts of his body as well as his internal organs. He must breathe to get oxygen and eliminate carbon dioxide and he must now use his own excretory organs to get rid of potentially toxic waste products. These activities will usually proceed quite automatically and quite efficiently. At a somewhat higher level of function, certain events occur which signal the beginning of processes and relationships of great importance for the development of what we later refer to as the personality of the child. Not long after birth, it is aroused by painful sensations having origin in what we identify as hunger cramps. However much we may welcome his healthy bawling, we cannot but recognize that he is both frightened and enraged, and at all events, very unhappy and quite helpless to do anything about it. It is at this point that he will now face life as we more familiarly know it and first experience pain and pleasure in a structured but complex and discontinuous relationship with his environment. While within the body of his mother, events were in a continual ebb and flow, but now they are interrupted, phasic and uncertain.

3. *Growth and Change*

If, at this point, the infant were left to its own resources, it would die, despite its very powerful potentials for life. His dependency upon others for satisfaction of his vital needs remains but in contrast to the situation before birth, these needs must be consciously anticipated and understood by the mother and others and require voluntary action on their part. This means that there will be delays between the times needs arise and the times satisfactions will be achieved. It also means that there is a greater possibility for failures, out of error on the part of the agencies responding to the child, or at least because of reactions quite out of context of the child's needs and demands. What we are witnessing are the beginnings of "socialization" of the child; socialization in the sense that the quality of the relationship between the child and the environment involves communication through signals and symbols which must first be *interpreted* and then acted upon by other organisms. The beginnings of "social behavior" are therefore to be found in the early parent-child relationships, and in many respects these are little different from those to be found among animals and birds. The difference lies largely in the potentials which the child possesses in contrast to those in lower forms of life and in the long and complex interdependency which prevails in human family life.

There are certain special features of these early relationships which now deserve our attention if we are to understand what growth and maturation involve. For some time after birth, the infant does not perceive objects in its environment. It experiences sensations and reacts with certain physical responses which constitute feeling states. These may be pleasant or painful and we can usually distinguish these by the behavior of the child. It is the behavior of the child which provides us with signals to which we respond by doing those things which we feel are needed, especially as regards relieving the pain or discomfort which we assume caused his crying. For the infant, this establishes a relationship, not with mother, but with a sequence of events experienced within its Self;

for example, hunger(pain) — crying (signal) — nursing (relief). At this point, he does not recognize mother as such, nor the fact that the relief he experienced was due to something outside and separate from himself, acting independently (however altruistically) on his behalf. Even as his sensory apparatus is developing, bringing ever more definite visual and auditory impressions to its central nervous system, it continues to act "as if" all these were parts of itself — as if there were no boundaries between itself and the world. In such a state, he is, as it were, the center of a universe which is merely an extension of self, and we recognize this as a natural order of transition from his state while yet in the body of his mother. With the passage of time and the progressive alterations brought about by growth, experience and learning, he becomes slowly aware that there are objects beyond himself, having an independent existence of their own and not functioning entirely under the influence of his needs. Where previously he felt omnipotent to relieve his own painful states and fulfill his own needs, he now begins to see that he is dependent upon objects outside himself and that he does not have the power he thought he had to control things. This insight does not come suddenly nor dramatically and produce a completely reordered construction of his relationship with self and objects. This is so because he does not yet possess the backlog of experiences and the intellectual capacity to make evaluations which in adults would lead to generalizations which in turn become guides to conduct. The child at this stage is still governed by primitive, biologically determined modes of experiencing, and though he now begins to accept the existence of objects outside itself, he clings to the assumption that these objects exist for his benefit and are magically subject to his wishes. We speak of him as being narcissistic and describe his relationship with objects as being ego-centered. However much his toothless grins and babbling are a delight to his parents, we must recognize (without moralizing or censoring) that he is completely self-centered, and his pleasures he takes for granted. He is capable of demands and of rage when frustrated. If he gives pleasure, it is only because he is pleased with himself and we as adults take pleasure in his behavior. He is this way because of his stage of life.

Obviously, this state of affairs cannot continue unchanged for very long. As he gains in size, strength and motor skills, he inevitably bumps against the sharp edges of reality. He learns that painful or pleasant sensations, though felt within himself, derive from his contact with objects, which have a variety of qualities. He learns which are likely to be hot or cold, smooth or rough, bitter or sweet. He comes to recognize objects by other qualities than their visualized forms. And soon he encounters an array of prohibitive injunctions comprising the "do's and don'ts" laid down by parents and others in his world. He is restrained from the free exercise of his desires and discovers that if he persists in doing what has been forbidden he may be punished. This is a bitter and as yet incomprehensible experience; he is not only prevented from doing as he pleases, but an adult with whom he has experienced pleasure now causes him pain. Parents, who previously appeared to function for the sole purpose of pleasing him and easing his pains, now loom as frustrating, unreliable, inconsistent and hurtful creatures. He cannot comprehend why he should not be free to do what he wishes — the concepts of good, bad, nice, naughty, clean, dirty, etc., do not exist for him. These have yet to be learned and the process is often most painful. Learning is reinforced by punishment for unacceptable behavior and reward for good behavior. He learns to accept delays in satisfaction of needs, even to accept substitute gratifications at times, and not infrequently some defeats. He begins to grasp "the rules of the game" and within the limits of his ability he becomes a player. With this, he slowly emerges and grows beyond the narcissistic, ego-centered attitudes of his earlier days. This is not to say that he suddenly becomes an angel of altruism and self-denial. If he accepts the existence and rights of others, he nevertheless most zealously protects his own. He'll play the game, but will do no more than his share and be vehement in his reaction to what he regards as unfair on the part of others. He will be a stickler about rules, whether in games with his friends or in the assignment of chores at home. He may learn to earn favors and affection, and even show a little appreciation thereof, but we should not be surprised if there is little evidence of deep gratitude for or long remembrance of the rewards and gifts he is given. More often his demands seem insatiable and his capacity for generosity non-existent. He often resents favors shown to others and in outrage, challenges his parents' love for him. These are difficult times, as every parent knows, but even if he is not a very generous or grateful person, he is on his way to acquiring some frustration tolerance and the socialization of his attitudes and values.

By way of brief summary, let us at this point see the human organism in terms of his growth and evolution from the time of conception to this present period. We must keep in mind the nature of his origin, the structural changes he undergoes, the environment in which this takes place and the events which must occur as he inter-acts with his environment. For the purpose of this book, the most important thing to keep in mind is the "attitudinal orientation" of the organism — *narcissistic, ego-centered* — and recognize that this is quite normal because of the very nature of its experiences and its limited resources for understanding them. We must also recognize the changes in this attitudinal orientation as growth and learning proceed.

4. *From Self-Love to Object-Love*

The child is now ready for a new order of inner experiences which permit a higher level of critical judgment of himself and his world. He discovers that it is much more fun to play with friends than to play by himself. Loneliness takes on a deeper and more poignant quality, and if quarrels and altercations seem to make for rather stormy and discontinuous allegiances, we also note how quickly rifts are repaired and how hungry he is for companionship. We also see that value judgments, however crude or illogical, enter into his personal choices. He becomes more selective of his friends and develops reasons for his choices. Those of whom he approves, and who approve of him, become objects of special treatment. To safeguard and maintain the alliance he may now show the first real signs of spontaneous generosity. He discovers the pleasures of sharing and the pleasures of giving. In games he feels more secure in the team relationship and is happy when his contribution is accepted and praised. He finds himself offering favors to others and their own pleasure delights him. He is also more directly aware of times when he feels hurt, sick and lonely; when he needs comforting, reassuring and tender (but wordless) affection. He turns for this to his parents with trust and confidence. It is not an imperious demand in the sense of his infant expectations, but a mixture of things — hope, fear, loneliness and bewilderment — the child has tasted the feelings of a man and seeks again to be a child. When he is held by a parent, soothed and reassured, there wells within him a surge of emotion he cannot define, but which enables him to see the parents in a new light — the light of love. This is still not "adult love," but an important forerunner thereof. His feelings at this moment involve such things as are akin to awe and reverence. The parent is no longer a servant to his needs. And the world is no longer only an extension of self. He has become cognizant of his relative helplessness in a world that is complex, unpredictable and potentially dangerous. The desire to retreat, to withdraw, is powerful when all seems bitterness and chaos, and from deep within himself are remembrances of things past which move him to seek the shelter of his mother's womb. The best he can do is blindly reach out and when either parent responds by holding him, rocking him and uttering of words of comfort, order is restored and the new vision of his parents brings

with it the first real experience with what we call
"object-love."

The capacity for object-love (as contrasted with self-
love) does not appear suddenly, nor full-grown. It
remains rooted in its forerunner and must endure many
challenges and vicissitudes which threaten to over-
whelm it. Given a chance, however, it too grows and
flourishes in time. Certain people and even certain
institutions begin to assume a significance and importance which move him to acts of generosity and later
even to sacrifice of his possessions or of himself in the
service thereof. Now it is that we begin to see the
man within the boy and the woman within the girl;
to see within the bud the potential that with careful
nurturing can come to full flower. The seed bore little
resemblance to the young plant, and now the bud has
but little likeness to the flower, but the potential is
always there. What we are now aware of in the child,
in the man-to-be, are qualities and capacities which
can uniquely dignify his existence as a human organism, distinct from all other forms of life. Arising out
of the inadequacy of self-love and the egocentric object-
relationships of early childhood comes a seeking for
deep and abiding relationships, and if the residual of
self-interest still colors much of his behavior, we must
recognize that with maturation he is learning that he
cannot live for them alone. His growing awareness of
the mysteries of Life and Death, of the enormous universe of time and space, and of the uncertainties in his
personal destiny produces sober contemplation and
arouses within him his greatest potential for human
achievement, his capacity for love — love of mate, children, group, mankind and his personal God.

5. *The Role of Instincts*

Among the more controversial subjects in the behavioral sciences is that dealing with so-called Instincts
and Instinct Theory. Few terms have provided so
much fuel for the fires of scientific debate. Nor has
the battle been confined to the private domain of the
academician. The clergy and the man-on-the-street
are frequently concerned with the meanings of this
term and at times bitter controversy has been waged in
the name of "Morality," "Will-power," "Responsibility"
and the like by those who would attempt to explain
man's origins and account for his behavior.

I have no desire to engage my colleagues or others
in such controversy, but because much is made of
Instincts, I feel there is a place for some consideration
of this subject in a book of this kind; for the purpose of
improving or clarifying our understanding of those
vague forces within us which seem to impel us to
action with little direction from our conscious controls.

We have little difficulty in accepting the idea that
a seed, properly nurtured, will grow from a single cell
into a complex multi-celled and multi-organed living
creature. The accumulating technical knowledge of
how this takes place need not involve us in metaphy-
sical or theological issues. Most of us are quite content
with the answers of geneticists, biologists, physicists
and chemists which yield practical and logical descrip-
tions of the phenomena without detracting from the
beauty and awesome mysteries of ultimate causes.
We accept the fact that transformations and energy
exchanges take place which determine the particular
physical characteristics of a given type of organism.

And most of us are more or less content with the simple view that "forces" are at work accomplishing these miracles without a "mental" apparatus within the cell to direct the undertaking. It is when we deal with organisms of more complex form, and especially with human behavior, that our understanding becomes clouded by issues and questions most difficult to resolve.

For my purposes I would recommend that we take our point of departure from that which we have already accepted, namely, that from the beginning of life, forces are set in motion which make growth and development possible. Further, that despite the initial momentum afforded by physical and chemical reactions taking place as a result of the union of sperm and ovum (conception), the cell will die unless it is provided with things it needs. These needs will continue, though vary in kind, throughout the life of the organism. The tissues of our bodies will always be requiring a supply of materials from the outside and also the means of getting rid of their own waste products. The rate at which this takes place is not constant, either from moment to moment, day to day, or year to year. When the rate increases markedly we recognize what we have called "tissue needs". These may be for oxygen, sugar or other substances vital to the life of individual cells and the functional effectiveness of tissues and organs. We saw earlier that while within the body of his mother these needs were satisfied without any conscious effort on the part of the child. Later on, these needs give rise to patterns of stimulation which reach the brain and set in motion learned responses which end in organized, goal-directed behavior whereby the materials needed by the body are procured. Viewed in developmental sequence, we see the following pattern of change: the unborn child automatically receives what it needs from the blood-stream of the mother which is directly connected with that of the baby via the umbilical cord; after birth, the material must enter the body via the mouth, which requires sucking and swallowing (acts which occur reflexly, but later come under voluntary control); with growth and learning, the organism responds to the pattern of stimulation we call hunger by going to the sources of supply and selecting edible materials which it then eats; still later, we see behavior indicating that the organism will engage in "food-getting" even in the absence of immediate tissue needs, e.g., when mother goes to the grocer's to buy food for herself and family for the week, she has anticipated needs which will arise in the future.

What all this means is that from the time of conception until the end of life, we have needs and that these needs give rise to behavior aimed at obtaining satisfactions; that with learning, the behavior comes to be more and more under conscious control and to operate in the absence of immediate tissue needs, in anticipation of their recurrence in the future. In this context, Instinct is not a thing as such, but an *evolving system of processes by means of which the organism acts to satisfy its basic needs.*

Certain authors have worked out elaborate classifications of a great number of so-called instincts. Still others argue that there are really none. The real issue is not one of who is right and who is wrong, but of terminology and definition. I believe we need not belabor the question. In the light of our foregoing discussions, I believe we can accept without great difficulty the general thesis that *it is inherent in the nature of living things to preserve, if they can, their existence and to reproduce their own kind.* This is no less true of humans than it is of plants and animals. In the instance of human beings, however, we recognize that such instinctive behavior is progressively more under the control of our higher mental faculties, though we need not flatter ourselves that this in itself is either a uniquely distinguishing characteristic nor one which we always manage very successfully. This means that at times all creatures tend automatically to do those things which will serve the needs of self-preservation and of reproduction. At other times they will act as if in opposition to these fundamental desires. Animals as well as humans are capable of self-sacrifice in the service of others, particularly when protecting their young. And as for the sexual customs of animals in the wild state, there is ample evidence to indicate that their's make a lot more sense than do those of most human communities. At least among the lower animals there is consistency and logic, based upon seasonal and physiologic conditions plus the specific characteristics of the specie group-organization. It is curious to find that man, the higher primates and most domesticated animals seem to be much less stable in the management of sexual impulses than other forms of life.

If then we can accept the idea that living things do have powerful drives which concern themselves with self-preservation and reproduction, we may now turn our attention to a closer scrutiny of what we shall tentatively call the Sexual Instinct and psychosexual **development.**

6. *Psychosexual Development*

Few subjects have received as much attention as "sex." Few subjects have caused as much grief, argument or misunderstanding. No other expression of human behavior has been either so ruthlessly condemned or callously exploited. No other subject of importance to human existence has been more misrepresented by such a wide variety of self-appointed authorities. To some degree, this is changing, and for this we can thank a relatively few men who dared to study the subject with the same objectivity as that employed with any other behavioral phenomena. For much of this, we are indebted to Sigmund Freud; not so much for his specific theories, as for the singular fact that he brought the study of sex back to the field of science. What this really means is that if we are to talk about what man ought *to be* (problems of conduct, ethics, etc.), we must first know what he *is* and how he got this way. If sex and sexual behavior seem to have preoccupied much of Freud's thinking, this was in a large measure due to his realization of how little we understood the subject and how important it was that it be afforded the same careful study as any other biological and behavioral phenomena. More than that, his own investigations provided a generalization concerning sex that fitted precisely what had already been established as axiomatic in the biological sciences; namely, that to understand any adult organism we must study the history of the specie *and* of the individual. Stated more pointedly, the study of human behavior, including the sexual, must encompass the entire life of the organism — the patterns we display today are the products of the past and in infancy and childhood are the forerunners of the future. The sexual behavior of the adult has roots, too, in the beginnings of life.

To understand sexual behavior, we must be prepared to broaden our views and recognize that adult sexual behavior is only a stage in an evolutionary sequence that begins with conception and if it appears that infantile sexuality bears little resemblance to the adult forms, the difference is one of form rather than of subject and perhaps of our lack of perception.

From infancy onwards, the human organism experiences a variety of feelings — states arising from sensations it receives from various parts of its body. In the main, these are roughly pleasant or unpleasant and we soon discover that under the aegis of what Freud called the "Pain-Pleasure Principle" the organism seeks to avoid unpleasant experiences and seeks to repeat those that gave it pleasure. Painful sensation means that something is wrong — pain is ordinarily felt when tissues or organs are being injured and the sensation, like a warning signal, calls our attention to this and impels us to act to protect the offended part. Pleasure is in many ways a more complex matter, but I think we can easily accept the idea that all of us like to do that which does give us what we feel to be pleasure. With learning, the child discovers how to evaluate objects in terms of their association with painful or pleasurable results. However, in the beginning, he has some difficulty because the pain (or pleasure) is felt *in* his body though the object is somehow "out there." What he is led to discover is that his body or its part must participate in the experiencing process. At first glance, this would appear to be a rather pointless observation, but if we look beyond the obvious to the implications, we shall see rather significant possibilities. We have already found that in its earliest days the infant does not clearly distinguish its self from the world around it and the limiting boundaries of its own body have not yet been discovered. It is only with further development that this becomes possible. It comes relatively slowly and as a consequence of certain changes in its own capacities as well as certain experiences to which it is normally exposed.

Very early in life, he experiences pleasure in mouth activities (sucking and swallowing) and also associates these activities with relief from pain (hunger). Throughout life the mouth will remain a part of the body useful in the service of many needs, most of which are pleasurable. These include, chewing, tasting, swallowing, talking, smoking and of course, kissing. The mouth is the area by means of which we have our first meaningful contact with the environment and it maintains its high position of importance throughout life, not only as a physical part of the digestive tract, but as a source of pleasure and an agency for the expression of affection by words or kissing.

The discovery of the world is a discovery of sensations and only with time and repeated experience does the child begin to organize these sensory patterns into perceptions that relate to specific objects. Because sensation is experienced as being in or on the body, the discovery of the world begins with the discovery of one's own body; its physical boundaries, sensory capacities and motor functions. In addition to oral experiences, it discovers its hands and the pleasures of touching and grasping and conveying (especially to the mouth). He will search with his eyes and want to see new and often forbidden sights. He will come to recognize both painful and pleasurable sensations in relation to toilet functions. He will discover his sex organs. Of course, all this applies equally to little girls. There are numerous books which deal extensively with these phenomena, detailing the relationship they have with our character traits in later life. For our purposes, suffice it to say that sexual pleasure is mediated through many parts of our body and that the adult sexual act (intercourse) is but an end-stage of a developmental sequence. The deeper significance of this will be considered at a later time in the course of our study.

I wish now to dwell at some length on that sequence of events which reveals the progress of psychosexual development. The term psychosexual is used merely to emphasize that we are dealing with more than just physical growth and the maturation of specific organs. Attitudes, feelings and the state of knowledge the individual possesses at different stages of life are all part of the process. These derive from the interraction of his own drives and needs with the environment as structured by his family and the community.

I mentioned earlier that the child discovers its body, and that in the course thereof, he (or she) will discover the sex organs. This, in itself, means little to the child. It notes a relationship to urination and certain sensations attendant to this excretory function. It may also inadvertantly find that rubbing or pressing upon this area produces pleasant sensations, just as earlier he found pleasure in sucking. His awareness of his sex organs tends to be heightened from now on by the attitudes of others rather than by any dramatic or special changes in his sex organs. Parents remove his hands from his organs. He is gradually aware that this part of the body is kept concealed more than other parts. An atmosphere of mystery and uncertainty is fostered which sharpens his curiosity. He observes that the people around him have distinguishing characteristics by means of which he can tell one from the other. These characteristics involve size, shape, dress, facial appearance, voice and many others. He also realizes that they are different from him and as he progresses he wants to be more certain of what he is, and in what ways he is like they are. He comes to see that in addition to differences in general appearance among friends and family, there are also some puzzling similarities and common characteristics which seem to group people. He hears and sees things which permit him to make a distinction between boys and girls, and between men and women. At first, this is related to dress, hair styles and other surface phenomena, but as his curiosity continues and his perceptions sharpen, he seeks for more convincing and specific reasons. In the home, he will observe very quickly (opportunity permitting) that mother and father are physically different, and so are brother and sister. He begins to compare his body with that of others and soon learns that what determines whether one is a boy or a girl can be seen in the physical characteristics of that special area between the thighs and below the abdomen. Textbooks of psychology and psychopathology deal at length with the ramifications of this situation. For our purposes, I would only point out that children do concern themselves with these matters and it is normal for them to do so. It sets the stage for self-identity, for socialization and role-taking, and for later sexual functions. He (or she) can now really begin to be a little boy or little girl and get started on the long road learning their special roles and functions. They see that their parents are a male-female pair, and from stories they hear, observations of animal pets and the conduct of older children, they begin to sense the existence of a universal pattern — that somehow that special difference which makes one person male and the other one female creates conditions which bring them together. This leads to the first questions about babies and sex anatomy, and eventually to those about sexual relationships. The child is preparing itself for adulthood.

We can now see that just as the infant was moved along a course which took him from the period of self-love and ego-centered object relationships to object-love, so, too, must his sexual development follow a similar path. In infancy, he is concerned with self-pleasure. Later, he begins to find pleasure in sharing with others. With the emergence of mature object-love comes the desire to give pleasure to the loved subject. All of life has been a preparation for this; first came the self-preservation functions, then close behind them the sexual — the former dealing with the survival of the individual, the latter with the survival of the race. Certain steps and stages were necessary, each leading to the next and important for the successful attainment of maturity. If many individuals appear to be something less or achieve less, it is not because the potential was lacking (in otherwise normal individuals). The fault must lie in a rather tragic condition — that while learning is essential for maturation, we can learn wrong things as well as right things, and the remarkable faculties of memory, reasoning, and concept formation which distinguish man from beast can lead to misconceptions as well as "truth." When individuals fail to mature psychologically and socially, we can usually find the cause in the learning experiences afforded them by a family and a society which has not faced the psychobiological facts of life.

7. Early Experience and Adult Sexual Behavior

It is now time to examine in some detail the consequences of normal growth and development in the shaping of our sexual desires. We have already seen how each stage of life prepares us, well or not, for the next one and it is not difficult to conclude that early experiences together with powerful urges and social conventions would possibly have profound effects upon our attitudes and actions in adult life, and especially as regards sex.

We have already seen that in early infancy and childhood the organism discovers its body and the world about it, aided by the associated feelings of pain or pleasure which help to guide and teach it. Most of us today are able to face the fact that children have curiosity about sexual matters long before they can or do have sexual intercourse and that this curiosity is not only normal, but desirable as a means of preparing the child for later life.

If it were possible to place a pair of healthy babies on a deserted island and in some way enable them to survive without any human adult care, we would probably see a sequence of events which would dramatically demonstrate the "natural" evolution of sexuality. The children would grow, discover all the modalities of pain and pleasure, determine their own physical boundaries (body-image) and discover that of the other child's. They would note their physical differences and accept them as such. They would play and work together and cling to each other when fear or cold drew them together. With puberty, they would note the outer physical changes taking place in each other and would become conscious of pleasant sensations in their sex organs. Each would discover that rubbing these parts heightened the pleasure leading to a climax of intense feeling, followed by relaxation and calmness. Reawakened curiosity about their partner would lead to mutual petting and caressing with the inevitable realization that the very nature of the differences in their sex organs (principally the penis and vagina) invited an experiment which placed the one within the other. With this consumatory act, sexual maturity would be reached. The intense pleasure of intercourse, followed by the release of tension and the "oceanic" feeling thereafter would be repeatedly sought as the most preferred form of sexual behavior. In time, of course, pregnancy would ensue and a new society would be in being.

I have often presented this little fantasy to people and it is surprising how many are incredulous, even to the point of asking, "How would those children know what to do?", referring, of course, to the mechanical aspects of intercourse. In response to this, I find no need to dwell at length on the technical details which give us a scientific explanation. I merely point out that animals and primitive peoples require no formal instruction in these matters. That some parents need to be reminded of this, serves to emphasize the fact that civilization has produced some strange and distorted views of nature. Of more specific concern is the fact that in our anxiety to distinguish ourselves from animals and "savages," we have created something so completely false as to deny not only the nature of what we are, but also to render almost impossible what as humans we are uniquely capable of becoming in the fullness of maturity.

Psychosexual development can now be seen as a long-term process involving the total body and all the learning experiences of the individual organism. From infancy onwards, he is being prepared for that time when he is ready to join with a mate in that union of body and spirit epitomized in the act of sexual intercourse. I cannot emphasize too strongly the importance of our understanding of this feature of human growth and development, for it is in the mismanagement of the "sexual" experiences of the infant and the child through the attitudes of the parents and society that most sexual problems of later life arise. The effects of such faulty attitudes are to stunt the emotional growth and warp the value-systems of the growing organism, impeding his development and keeping him rooted in the narcissistic, ego-centric patterns of the child.

A further examination of the significance of psychosexual development is to be found in the actual conduct of sexual relationships as it is expressed in the lives of a mature couple. *It can be said that such a relationship is, on a given night, a recapitulation of the psychosexual development of the lives of each of the partners.* Let us examine this in some detail.

Varying in time for different couples, a period of abstinence from sexual intercourse brings about a gradual building-up of sexual tension (need). This will be manifested by heightened sensations in the sex organs and increased sensitivity to the physical proximity of the mate. Thus, there is awareness of one's own body and that of the partner. This leads to increased desire to see, touch and in turn to be seen and touched. The mouth shares in these preliminary acts through words expressing love and desire, and through kissing (often of the cheeks, neck, hands and other parts of the body of the beloved). All this is but a reliving of early modes of experiencing sensory pleasure, but now in an atmosphere of adult love as contrasted with narcissistic pleasure-seeking. These preliminaries serve a dual purpose: they allow us to satisfy old needs carried over from childhood and they prepare us for those acts which could only be properly consummated with physiological sexual maturity. Thus, as these acts continue, there is further increase in sexual desire, now more specifically experienced in the particular organs which serve the adult sexual functions. Erection of the penis signifies readiness of the male for the act of intercourse. In the female, readiness is indicated by intensely pleasurable sensations in her sex organs, plus a flow of secretion from glands in the area which lubricate the opening and permits easy entrance of the penis into the vagina. Thus the preliminary acts of seeing, touching, fondling and kissing prepare the couple for intercourse and these same acts, in infancy and childhood, helped prepare the individuals for adult sexuality. What now distinguishes the mature couple from others in this relationship is their sensitivity to the needs and pleasures of each other. Because "readiness" for intercourse is generally slower in appearing in the female than in the male, the latter must be able to determine when his mate has reached that point. The mature male is patient and learns to recognize the signs which denote such readiness in his wife. She in turn assists him, either by encouraging continuance of the preliminaries or by her unashamed communication of her readiness. This freedom of communication and mature concern for each other's pleasure is the hallmark of their maturity. In fact, it may be said of such people that the man fully realizes his masculinity in the fullness of satisfaction he gives his wife; and that the woman best realizes her femininity in her awareness of the climax she has produced in her husband. When both experience this together, they are indeed as one.

At this point, we would do well to examine certain aspects of "love-making" which appear to cause some couples concern and about which there are a number of serious misconceptions.

In the course of growing up our pleasure-seeking is guided by the way various parts of our bodies react to given experiences. Right and wrong, good and bad have no meanings to us until we encounter the rules and codes imposed by the family and society, consequently, our impulses and desires often lead us to actions which meet disapproval. This is most particularly true of childhood sexual behavior. The desire to put things in the mouth is usually accepted by parents, but *what* is put in the mouth may be quite a different matter.   Later, what may be looked at or touched and what may not be, also becomes a matter of parental decision.   What is so puzzling to the child is that the rules often catch him by surprise; he is not able to grasp their logic (or his parent's) and they are neither the same for all people nor are they equally applicable to him at all times.   As an infant and child he can be seen naked by almost anyone; in being bathed and diapered, he is exposed to and handled by any of several people.   In nursing, he sucks happily on the breast or bottle.   He can easily learn and accept the fact that hot things hurt and that bitter or sharp things had better be left out of one's mouth, but it makes no sense to him that the bigger he gets, the more he is forbidden to do the very things which were sanctioned earlier (nakedness, nursing).   The fact that these things were pleasant makes their prohibition all the more confusing.   When still later he begins to question these matters more closely, he finds that they now relate to what is referred to as "sex."   He is given some facts and guides, but much is left to his imagination, which in turn is influenced by his instincts, early experiences and the bits and pieces of information or misinformation he gathers from his peers.   He is apt to be confused by opinions on sex expressed by his parents or educators which, quite properly, emphasize love and the wonder of conception and birth.   But, he is also given, directly or indirectly, to feel that certain things are now dirty, unnatural or perverse.   It is as if to say, certain things which were permissible now are not, but the reasons for this are never clearly given or else are made on an arbitrary moral basis rather than a physiological or psychological one. In most, if not all of us, are desires which we either deny exist, or at best, recognize and restrain. When they are accepted and allowed in the sexual relationship, they tend to occur under remarkably different circumstances; (1) illicit or extra-marital relationships, (2) as exclusive sexual goals (in perversions), and (3) in very happily adjusted mature married couples. With this statement, we must now face the nature of these acts and how they can occur in such diverse situations.

From the pattern of pleasure-seeking that we saw evolving from infancy and childhood, we find clues to the understanding of this subject. The eyes, hands and mouth were the principal agencies for exploration of the world and served to make known the unknown. Value-judgments regarding experiences were made in terms of painful or pleasurable feelings associated with the objects encountered. As a result of the normal experiences of childhood, we retain not only the use of the above agencies for exploring, but also the desires of our earliest days which were associated with great pleasure. These include being naked, feeling warm, soft skin, rocking, sucking and seeing the objects from which pleasure is derived. As we grow older, we are disturbed and puzzled by the fact that some of these earlier modes of pleasurable experience become forbidden and there is an increasing restriction placed upon any activities involving the sexual areas of the body. Thus, we are left with the residual desires of the past, plus the continuing development of desires for exploring new possibilities of pleasure and excitement. In so-called necking and petting and the previously described preliminaries to intercourse, we observed the manner in which this finds expression. There are also present, whether we recognize it or not, desires for other experiences, arising out of the continuing need to explore the unknown and, by implication, the forbidden. This may involve little more than desires to see and feel the body and sex organs of the mate, or include such acts as mouth contact with various portions of the body, including the sex organs. Such acts may serve as further preliminaries to intercourse or may be used to achieve climax and satisfaction without intercourse. Knowing this, we can now study briefly the different conditions under which these acts tend to occur.

First, these acts are indulged in where the desires are quite conscious, but the acts are regarded as improper and forbidden in marriage. Such indulgence must therefore occur either premaritally or extra-maritally. For such men or women, these acts are associated with guilt and they fear to admit them or attempt them in marriage lest the mate react with shock or disgust. Under these conditions, we usually find that when the acts take place, the individual manages to rationalize his or her conduct by disavowing any feelings for his partner in the relationship, *and* by telling themselves that this relationship in no way affects his or her feelings of love and respect for the lawful mate. It is as if they feel these acts are dirty and have no place as an expression of love. By separating love and sex, they hope to gain some sanction for the acts and ease from their guilt.

Secondly, these acts are often the chief form of sexual gratification in those people who, for various reasons, have suffered certain severe emotional problems in their early years. Such people cannot establish mature, heterosexual love relationships and remain fixated at earlier stages of psychosexual development. We see this in the homosexual relationship and in any of the many forms of perversion.

Finally, we have said that these may and do occur in the lives of mature married partners. In view of the foregoing, this may seem almost illogical. We must remember that because a given act is repressed by an individual, frowned on by society or engaged in by "abnormal" individuals, does not mean that the act is in fact inherently bad or evil. Mature couples, in the privacy of their love-making, know no inhibitions, but are guided by the desires and needs each is able to satisfy in the other. It is always an act of giving, not of taking. Furthermore, in such couples these acts tend to be merely extensions of the preliminaries to intercourse, and as such, because of the realization of the completeness of their giving, may add to the intensity of the final climax they experience. Being aware that all desires are acceptable and that they remain acts of love makes for such a complete union that there can be no "repressed" desires, and no third party could possibly provide that which each is giving the other.

In very brief summary, we have attempted to describe the growth and evolution of sexuality in the human organism and to establish the general idea that any sexual act is neither inherently evil nor good, but that how we use it will be the determining factor. Mature love, with all we have seen it to mean, is the vital factor that enables a man and woman to join together, physically and spiritually, in such manner that there can be no wrong between them, for whatever they do is done as an act of love.

8. *Sex and Reproduction*

Thus far we have given no special consideration to the relationship between sexuality and reproduction. It goes without saying that under ordinary conditions the one is the means to the other. However, a number of questions pertinent to this issue must be faced by many people and therefore it is worthy of our attention.

It is with far more than academic interest that we face the fact that the sexual relationship and reproduction are quite distinct functions. At first glance this may seem to be an overstatement of the obvious, since we are well aware that intercourse does not always lead to pregnancy and that this may occur because of purely biological factors or because the couple uses contraceptives to prevent it. There are, however, deeper considerations which merit our scrutiny. There is evidence that some primitive cultures and probably all animals do not directly recognize the relationship between sexual intercourse and reproduction. This seeming failure to grasp what we accept so easily is quite understandable. Since a normal female is fertile during only a few days of each month over a limited number of years, it would be quite natural for primitive people to conclude that, since intercourse took place far more often than pregnancy, there was no causal relationship between them. It was inevitable that even they would arrive at a more accurate appraisal of the facts of life, but it is not hard for us to see the source of their original errors. Of even more importance to us is the fact that we can quite properly infer that early man engaged in sexual relationships primarily for pleasure and barely possibly for love. It is only with the growing realization of the relationship between intercourse and reproduction that more serious moral issues began to crystallize and these remain with us today. Awareness of the procreative power in the sexual act elevated the act and endowed it with mysterious meanings. Puberty took on important new dimensions. Family structure attained new significance. Complicated religious rites and codes developed to explain and control sexual behavior, many of which have been re-expressed in various ways in our contemporary legal codes and religious beliefs. Both law and religion define with whom we may have intercourse and make punishable any other relationship, but beyond this, we also see the pervasive effects of the special attitudes toward sexuality itself which are deeply rooted in much of western religious thinking. Thus, some believe we are conceived in sin and see in the sexual desire and act the key to the sinfulness of mankind. Others, while accepting the sexual relationship as natural and desirable, do so only if it be engaged in for the specific purpose of procreation. A still different view holds that the sexual act is natural and necessary and should be engaged in as long as the couple make no effort to prevent pregnancy. A larger number of people believe in the propriety of the use of contraceptives to control the frequency of pregnancy and leave the couple free to engage in coitus without fear of conception.

Whatever the special beliefs we may hold as individuals or as a group, we cannot deny the fact that knowledge and belief were not always as they are now and that in the beginning, before man learned of the relationship between coitus and conception, no such questions arose to vex him.

To complicate matters further, we now have experimental evidence to show that reproduction is possible not only without intercourse (via artificial insemination) but even without semination. Certain biologists have been able to reproduce rabbits without any male element (sperm cells). This is technically known as parthenogenesis and raises the delicate question of the possibility of so-called virgin-birth.

The point of all this is to face the question of sexuality and reproduction on a broad basis. There is no reason why a couple reared in a religious faith which forbids the use of contraceptives (or the avoidance of pregnancy by any other means than abstinence) could not be very happy and lead a very fulfilling life together. On the other hand, in the absence of such special beliefs, it would be very tragic if because of ignorance and misinformation such couples produced unwanted children in an atmosphere of shame, guilt and degradation. Healthy sex attitudes relate to healthy general attitudes towards life. Maturity involves awareness of privileges *and* responsibilities. Our bodies can make us aware of the tension of hunger and also of sexual desire. How we satisfy either is a matter of more than just opportunity. It must also involve a sense of values which can guide our choices and keep us fully conscious of the meanings and possible consequences of our actions. As it relates to sex, we can free ourselves from the idea that as such, sex is inherently dirty or sinful, but in its place we must see that its fullest and richest expression is realized only when it is the expression of mature object-love. Whatever our beliefs may be, they will not contradict that concept, and I am firmly convinced that for most of us, the presence of mutual love gives sanction to the natural expression of our most intimate desires, with or without reproduction as a goal.

9. *Pleasure is Not Enough*

Thus far, the reader may have been tempted to a somewhat cynical conclusion—that the author feels that pleasure-seeking is the ultimate aim in life and that, however much we may seek to justify and dignify it by giving pleasure to others, it remains pleasure-seeking and primarily selfish. I would wish immediately to correct any such impression and shall at this time try to carry the theoretical formulations forward to another and, I believe, higher level of evaluation of human behavior potentials.

Some years ago, the editors and publishers of Life Magazine assembled a group of scholars to discuss the nature of "happiness." The task was not an easy one and certainly produced no unanimity of agreement among all who were there. Lesser men might have been content with narrowly conceived and quite superficial definitions of happiness, but it has always been a characteristic attitude of sincere and scholarly minds that it is better to leave a question unanswered than to reply with what they cannot believe in sincerely, and that the existence of contrary opinions by their peers means only that the correct answer has not yet been revealed. Be that as it may, I feel we must make some further effort to gain a better understanding of that word, so commonly used and so variously defined.

Our founding Fathers spoke of certain inalienable rights. One of these, they asserted, was the pursuit of happiness. We quite properly assume that these were men of good will, and possessed of sufficient knowledge and seriousness of purpose so that we would not hastily conclude that this phrase was included either as a pretty embellishment to their stately prose or as a permissive declaration to encourage self-indulgence without regard for the person or property of others. In their wisdom, they left undefined the word "happiness" and we note that they did not say man is entitled to happiness, but only the *pursuit* thereof.

Viewed in the broad context of the Constitution and the Bill of Rights, it is not difficult to discern the intentions of the authors in their decision to include the phrase "the pursuit of happiness." It must have been apparent to them that no State nor any individual can guarantee happiness for anyone, and that each of us must seek our own. However, in their wisdom, they further recognized that a democratic society could not exist if each man were completely free to do as he pleased in the exercise of *his* "right." The problem was to integrate the desires of the individual with those of the group, under a system of rules which would afford protection for society, and yet not stultify and cripple the individual. That they (and we) were not altogether successful is obvious, but I find no cause for quarrel with their approach nor with their concept; for what they apparently recognized was a potential in both the individual and in society—a potential for maturity that could lead men and states to a higher level of accomplishment and fulfillment. It is dangerous to draw analogies between man the organism and the collectivities of organisms which form groups or nations, but I see a close parallel in this specific area and believe that the drafters of our Constitution also recognized it. To me this is implicit in the idea of *the pursuit of happiness (not pleasure!) under law.* It remains for us to attempt to establish a useful concept of happiness and test its validity for man and the state. To do this, we must return to the study of the human organism, with special emphasis on the psychobiologic concept of "pleasure." If this seems rather remote from the subject as expressed in the title, I would beg the reader's indulgence and hope that he will hear me out, for *it is only with a basic understanding of pleasure in the psychologic sense that we can begin to discuss happiness.*

There is already a vast amount of literature dealing with the physical and chemical processes of living tissues. Much of this has tended to demonstrate that these processes comprise dynamic systems which somehow resist change—as if they wished to maintain a "steady-state" of equilibrium (homeostasis). When these systems are stressed by over-loading or by deprivation of needed supplies, attempts are made to compensate for the imbalance and return to the earlier state. The stresses which tend to upset the equilibrium of the various systems within the body may arise from external conditions acting upon the organism or they may arise from within the body itself. An example of the former would be excessive summer heat causing heavy loss of fluid and salt from the body. An example of the latter would be simple hunger or thirst.

Whatever the cause may be, the disturbance of equilibrium produces what we call *tension* in the involved systems. At some level of tension, chemical and/or physical reactions are induced which stimulate responses in the organism designed to reduce the tension and restore the equilibrium. Thus, the presence of excessive carbon dioxide in the blood stream will stimulate the respiratory centers of the brain, causing us to breathe more rapidly and deeply and, in so doing, we wash out the excess carbon dioxide and obtain the needed oxygen. With this accomplished, we breathe more easily once again. Many such automatic reactions are in operation all the time and rarely do they cause us anything more than mild feelings of discomfort for brief periods. However, some are apt to be painful, forcing into consciousness an awareness of serious trouble which will require complex deliberate action if we are to correct it. Thirst requires the search for water, as well as the act of drinking. Real danger from external sources demands careful selection of behavioral responses. But the very awareness of danger may evoke such profound and rapid reactions that we may become panic-stricken or even faint; as if the body was suddenly flooded with such an intensity of painful sensations that automatic responses of a primitive nature overwhelmed us and we were unable to exercise reason to guide our behavior. In other circumstances, we encounter what appears to be paradoxical in our handling of tension: there are times when we quite deliberately seek to increase our tensions. We often delay satisfying our need for food (hunger) in order to enjoy better a Thanksgiving dinner—so called whetting the appetite. We may engage in risky undertakings, courting danger for the thrill. Two things are involved in these situations: (1) an assumption that eventually the need can be satisfied or the danger avoided, and (2) recognition that relief of tension is a pleasant state. If the tension is permitted to build up, without too much real danger to the organism, then the relief is that much greater and our pleasure increases proportionately, producing the sensation of "thrill" or pleasurable excitement. Tensions may, therefore, be seen in terms of relatively simple biological needs or complex psychological needs, all of which produce some degree of discomfort and stimulate us to some form of action. The satisfaction of these needs reduces the tension and gives rise to pleasant sensations. Deliberately delayed satisfactions increase the tension and consequently the pleasurable state that follows.

In what we have just concluded, we see the basis for what we recognize as pain or pleasure. Obviously, for most of our waking lives we utilize experience to guide our behavior so as to minimize the number of painful situations and enhance the possibilities for pleasure. In short, pleasure is largely a matter of rather primitive sensations deriving from the relief of tensions which arise from disturbances in the dynamic equilibrium of complex systems in the body. One might wonder about that pleasure which comes from such abstract experiences as listening to music, watching a sunset or reading a poem. For many people there are needs for these things, and if they are not as imperious as hunger or thirst, they do have a place of importance in the hierarchy of needs and as sources of pleasure. Inactivity produces boredom which in turn produces tensions. How we relieve our boredom will vary from person to person, and may range from playing poker to listening to a symphony.

Obviously, learning plays a great role in shaping our awareness of what is apt to cause pain or pleasure. In infancy, it is often merely a matter of identifying things in terms of their physical properties—such as hotness, sharpness, softness or sweetness.   Later, through parents and others, we meet the schedule of "do's and don't" which limits our pleasure-seeking and the range of new experiences. We even encounter frustration and punishment without being sure of just why. Our needs are no longer immediately gratified. We must learn to delay satisfaction or even find substitutes which are acceptable both to us and to society.   In this context, we begin to acquire value-systems of a very complex nature; such as gaining pleasure from parental approval when we comply with their rules and give up something we wanted.   It is this capacity which eventually enables us to do many dull, tiresome or even painful things in life; to work hard for later rewards, to make personal sacrifices and at times even risk our very lives.

It is now time to establish our concept of pleasure as a lead to a definition of happiness. Pleasure involves satisfaction of needs (tension-relieving operations) and in infancy there is a demand for and expectation of immediate gratification. When needs are satisfied as they first make themselves felt, we can easily see that the temporal duration of either pain or pleasure would be brief. The memory of painful experiences is apt to be sharper than that for pleasant ones, but in neither case can we ever fully recapture the full flavor and intensity of the original experience through memory alone. Memory can only remind us of the past and incite us to action—usually the pursuit of some pleasure. There is yet another dimension of the "pain-pleasure" principle which must be mentioned. We seek to avoid painful experiences and we strive to repeat those which give pleasure, but a strange thing happens; if the same mode of pleasure-giving behavior is repeated too often or in too rapid succession, we tire of it, grow bored and look for new sources of excitement. A glance at those about us will reveal many people who are seemingly preoccupied with a kind of desperate search for pleasure; momentarily pausing at each new thrill, then, quickly surfeited, they move on and on. This perpetual flight is evidence of an infantilism carried over into adult life. Recalling our earlier discussion of the characteristics of infancy and early childhood, we can see now that *pleasure-seeking as such is related to egocentrism:* to the primitive, self-centered orientation of our earliest years, when objects had value only in terms of what they could do for us.

We noted earlier that maturity brought with it not only a need for others, but a capacity to love others even more than ourselves. We found also that self-gratification is not enough for the mature person and that he comes to find pleasure in the pleasure he gives to others. Now we can begin to see something of the nature of happiness. *In contrast to pleasure, which involves gratification of our own needs, that higher order of pleasure which derives from what we do for others gives us the key to the meaning of happiness.*

Where pleasure is temporary, fleeting and ephemeral, *happiness is a general state of satisfaction with a "way of life."* It springs from an inner awarness of our personal struggle against the continuing demands of an earlier self and the harsh realities of life. It is a sense of triumph tempered with humility — a triumph over one's self and a realization of the best of life through others; that in abandoning the self-centered universe of childhood, in losing ourselves, we most surely achieve a richer, deeper and more enduring satisfaction.

This is not to say that the mature person no longer enjoys and desires pleasurable experiences, nor to assert that happiness is a fixed state or goal which when reached produces a perpetual tranquillity. It is an on-going process of extension of Self; of constant learning, preparation and seeking with acceptance of reality in the fullness of its possibilities for joy and sorrow, for fulfillment and tragic disappointment, for simple pleasures and awe-filled contemplation of life's mysteries. This acceptance is not to be confused with resignation nor with blind faith. It is an acknowledgment of reality and an acceptance of its deepest challenge — the challenge not merely to endure, but to make existence meaningful. *The immature man or woman can never be happy! They can only know pleasure;* a brief moment of respite from boredom or terror. The mature person reaches out to life and does not seek escape. He knows that as an individual he may accomplish very little, but he does not abandon the effort and live only for himself. What then enables him to do all this. It is his capacity to love; his capacity to love his mate, his children and his fellow-man. Wise indeed was the poet who said, "All things that are loved are beautiful," be it mate, children, or life itself.

Happiness, therefore, stands in relation to pleasure, as object-love does to narcissism. Happiness and object-love are the products of an emergent, dynamic evolution, potential in the specie and in each individual. However imperfect mankind may be, we sense the profound changes he has undergone since his beginnings in pre-history. However much we fail to live up to our own ideals, we acknowledge and record them. Our libraries, art museums, concert halls, schools and churches are the repositories of those ideals. We pay no honor to the villains of history, but to the creative, inspired few who show us what we can become. It is this potential in each of us that gives us hope and it is the capacity to learn that makes it possible. The capacity to love gives meaning and purpose to our labors, igniting within us what Einstein called "a holy curiosity." Happiness is a thing called love.

10. *Friendship and Courtship*

From what has gone before us, we might easily say that much of life up through the teens is a preparation for love, sex and marriage, differing for each sex only in terms of the special functions each serves. Friendships arise out of the inadequacy of self-love and prepare us for membership in the larger community as well as for more private interpersonal relationships. With members of our own sex, we learn more about ourselves; our assets and liabilities — and what we want to be. Boys help to establish their identities as men as they talk and do things together. Girls confide in each other and help each other to consolidate their own special identities. In the course of all this, things do not go smoothly. The relationships vary in intensity and durability and disappointments are common. We discover that some people we like, do not equally like us. And some who seek our friendship do not appeal to us. First impressions backfire, leaving us discouraged with the one we trusted or with our own judgments. We begin to realize that it takes time to "get to know" someone and we become a bit more cautious about our choices and our behavior. Egocentrism tends to hang on and influence these choices, but it is diminishing and the capacity for object-love slowly develops.

During the teens, there is a great need "to belong." Being neither child nor adult, teenagers cling together for mutual support; pooling their collective grievances against the adult world and giving vent to their feelings in the full exuberance and artless manner of youth. Their energy, strength, new freedoms and awakening to the threshold of adulthood drive them to new experiences, not the least of which are with members of the opposite sex. There is excitement in this and if many seem carried away by their impulses and opportunities, there are those whose perspectives and judgment enable them to enjoy their high school years without falling into the stereotype so offensive to many adults. For these, the really maturing youngsters, this is a time of inner growth; a crystallizing of ideas, hopes and ambitions; a more perceptive awareness of self and others; the beginning of a deeper sensitivity to life. Friendships grow on the basis of more significant values, and those that are formed are less vulnerable to the inevitable pressures, disagree-

ments and shifting alliances of unstable groups.   In
all of us, however, is a deeply-seated inner fear of
loneliness and of incompleteness. When this is coupled
with maturing sexual impulses and the local peer-group
attitudes, it is not difficult to understand the restless,
awkward venturing of youth and the high increase
of "problem" situations. The more stable youngsters
are characteristically more goal-oriented and therefore
are less likely to be drawn into activities and situations
which might endanger their futures. They have all
the needs and desires of normal youth, but their perspectives and controls not only enable them to tolerate
frustration better, but to make value-judgments in
terms of longer-ranging possibilities. In boy-girl relationships, they tend to get less heavily involved with
any one person; preferring broad contacts and avoid-
ing entanglements. Some do "go steady" for long
periods, but with these couples there is a depth and
sincerity generally lacking in the relationships between
other couples. It is apt to be more open; shared not
only with the peer group, but with their families as
well.

These young people desire and enjoy affection.
Necking and some petting is commonplace, but tenderness and considerateness are there as well as passion,
and this helps to control the latter. It would be foolish
to deny that such couples ever have sexual relationships. Some do, and occasional "accidents" do occur,
but the incidence tends to be lower than for the rest
of the group. Usually limits are set by consent and
understanding. Such intimacies as are permitted are
gifts exchanged in an atmosphere of love rather than
goals for personal gratification to be bragged of later

before the gang. For this couple, this whole relationship is a new voyage of discovery, in the course of which old needs are rediscovered and new dimensions of experience are found. It is a process of getting to know the other person and one's self in terms of adjusting to each other and the whole wide world. This couple may never marry, but they are preparing themselves for it by learning the significant values of life.

Before moving on to the discussion of actual courtship and the formal preliminaries to marriage, we would do well to consider certain experiences which to some degree we all encounter. Often in the course of our growing up and with the first flowering of a capacity for object-love, we find ourselves preoccupied with strangely intense and often bitter-sweet feelings that attach themselves to a friend, an older person or even some remote person who may know us casually or not at all. In some instances, we may dare not reveal the presence of our yearnings, or they may be expressed with an intensity that is almost unbearable. These may involve members of the same sex or not. They may involve an older friend of the family, a teacher, a movie star or other prominent personality. Whichever object is chosen, the relationship is endowed by us with a magical and almost mystical quality that elevates it, removing it from the commonplace and possessing such significance as to be beyond the comprehension of mere mortals such as parents and peers.

The most familiar of these are the so-called "crushes" which develop between members of the same sex. Suddenly, and as if by magic, two girls or two boys are "best friends." A bond is formed, never to be broken. Utmost loyalty and devotion are demanded and the partners vie to out-do each other in the demonstration of their faithful attendance. Their communications are highly personal, secretive and exclusive. In public they exchange feelings and opinions by glances and gestures having special meanings to them alone. They marvel at their intuitive grasp of each other's thoughts and the harmony of their views on people, places and things. They move in a world of their own from which they look down upon ordinary mortals with an admixture of humor and contempt. It is a time for sharing and exchanging material belongings, knowledge and opinions. Discussions are endless and are often concerned with intimate topics, revealing personal experiences and feelings and providing opportunity to trade information about sex. If at times these "crushes" lead to more serious involvements of a homosexual nature, in most instances they are a normal part of growing up, representing a step in the direction of more mature object-relationships. They provide preliminary experiences with the deeper emotions and human values which will be the touchstones of success in marriage.

Occasionally, these relationships are more one-sided and are based upon hero-worship. Most of us have little chance to distinguish ourselves in the role of the star athlete or, in the case of girls, to be the class beauty. These images of an idealized self inevitably attract a coterie of slavish admirers. In the reflected glory of the central figure and in being part of the "in group," we increase our own stature. The competitive struggle to be "in" and to be close to the star may become fierce, leading to bitter rivalry and an excessive catering to the whims of the hero. This is not a healthy state either for the object of such attention or for the competitors. However, most youngsters do not get too deeply involved and soon sense the limitations of their heroes and the importance of maintaining their own self-respect as individuals.

A different type of attachment and one more likely to remain partially if not entirely concealed is to be found where a young boy or girl feels drawn to an older and relatively inaccessible person. They may range from fantasied romances with a reigning TV star to one with a teacher or friend of the family. Here the emotions may be quite intense and weighted with varying degrees of erotic desires. Younger children are more apt to see themselves in rather chaste relationships, the very purity of which makes them not only more acceptable, but even hopefully attainable. Teenagers are more apt to find their fantasies containing sexual material and, in their reveries, experiencing a variety of intimacies. At times these preoccupations are quite disturbing. In secret, they dream their dreams, frequently accompanied by masturbation, leaving them filled with restlessness, yearning and guilt. This, too, is part of growing up, helping us to clarify our desires and orient us on the map of life. Thus, through fantasy, we may in part see the reality we seek.

Finally, I would like to mention a rather special and wonderful experience common to nearly all of us. Unlike the relationships just described, this more nearly approximates adult relationships and in fact is modelled thereon. Rare is the man or woman who cannot look back upon the time of youth with some feeling of nostalgia and humor as they recall a chapter which might well be entitled "first love." It is as if all that had gone before suddenly crystallized and became meaningful; as if everything else was but preparation for this. The whole purpose of life becomes instantly clear and the focal point of existence is found in the radiant image of the other person. If, in retrospect, that special girl or boy has been divested of the magic glow, it is not because each was not as we saw them, but because *we* have changed. Then we were "ready" for love. Our very readiness and our needs, responding to those in the other person, brought into being what had been but a vague dream. "First love" is unique. There can never be another like it. Why? Because it was first. Does that mean it was best? No. But it was important and gave us our first real experience with adult emotions and object-centered mature love. Being first, it was yet too close to the time of ego-centered existence. Being first, it came before experience and time could temper knowledge with wisdom. And being first, it found us yet awkward and unskilled in the ways of life and love. If the rules and regulations governing the conduct of this relationship vary from generation to generation, and they do so but slightly, the feelings and general behavior of the participants vary scarcely at all. In these preposterously wonderful days, the love-sick youngsters are recognizable anywhere and need no description. Occasionally, these "first love" affairs endure and terminate in marriage. More often, the inevitable drift of days, changing interests, separations and new faces bring the relationship to an end. If for some there is disenchantment or heartbreak, for most there is unvoiced relief and an eager turning to fresh experiences in a larger framework of living.

For most of us, experiencing any or all of these attachments common to adolescence, they are merely anticipations of the future. In fantasy and feeling states we explore the world of romantic possibilities and more clearly sense the ultimate goals for which we strive. The harshness of reality is somewhat softened by our vision of what could and ought to be and in our youthful dreams we find a measure of meaning for tender love, fidelity and devotion. If such dreams seem to disappear and if a disproportionate share of our modern youths seem hardened, cynical and self-centered, the fault is not their's alone. We and the world we have made give little comfort to dreamers. For the able youngster the dream is but an inner image of what he may have perceived in the marriage of his parents. Guided by this, he explores the world of friendship and is unencumbered by any desperate need for attachment. Relationships come easily, but deepen slowly. Detachments may be somewhat painful, but are never catastrophic. When closeness develops with a member of the opposite sex, it is more broadly based and is neither guided by nor dependent upon sexual activities alone. Limits are set by agreement and yet there is frank acknowledgment of the needs and desires. If sexual intercourse does take place, there is likelihood of some forethought to the meanings of what they are doing and their responsibilities to each other. If we do not endorse such relationships, at least we can recognize that there can be a difference between these young people and those thrill-seekers for whom sex is an empty caricature of love.

When a mature couple is at last able to consider marriage, they will have already discovered many things about themselves, not the least of which are their imperfections and lack of agreement on all matters. What they will also recognize is that this is quite normal and that problems are a test of their maturity rather than a contradiction thereof. They will soon discover that when disagreements and misunderstandings stir up anger and resentment, egocentrism may send them furiously racing off in opposite directions, but very shortly they regret their hasty actions. Loneliness and a feeling of being incomplete soon alters their perspective on the causes of the rift and reunion occurs. They have learned that what draws them together is far stronger and more desirable than what drives them apart and they recognize that the better thing to do when problems arise is to "fight it out or work it out," but never run away. Thus, from even very painful experiences comes a knowledge that will be a solid foundation for their life to come. They are now most surely beginning to know each other and with this, they are preparing themselves as they move toward marriage.

As the couple acknowledges love and become engaged, they will have explored and continue to examine each other's attitudes and beliefs over a wide range of subjects. These will include problems of economics, occupation, homemaking, children, hobbies, health and probably sex. Together they will air their views and even seek guidance from others. They will communicate their love, but also their hopes and their fears, so that they will not only know each other better, but gain experience and confidence in the communication process itself. Planning for the future is part of the fun of being engaged and long discussions are frequent, but it is not only the prospect of the future which concerns couples. Each has a past, a background of experiences and conditions which may be of concern to them because of their possible bearing on the future of the relationship. Each may wonder how *much* to tell and *how* to tell of those things which in some way may be unpleasant.

Generally, there is some reluctance to reveal family "secrets," but in time these are usually aired. These may range from eccentricities of individuals to so-called scandals. In general, these can and should be communicated so that the partner may feel more secure in his knowledge of his in-laws and so that the couple may be better prepared to cope with them. Adverse attitudes on the part of parents must be identified and understood. The mature couple wants to know why these adverse attitudes are present, so they can be guided by them if they are found to be justified in some way, and adjust to them if they cannot be dispelled. They will be strong enough to face the hostile parent and attempt to modify the situation. If the parent is adamant, they will be strong enough to stick together and not allow the attitude of the parent to affect their feeling for each other. They will not act in haste, nor will they "blow up" merely for the sake of creating a dramatic scene. The problem must be talked through and the ways and means found for best managing an unhappy situation.

Another topic for discussion concerns medical problems which may have a bearing on the marriage. The presence of certain so-called familial diseases or a high incidence of chronic disease in either family should be made known. The wise couple will seek competent medical guidance regarding the nature of these conditions and their possible significance as it relates to the health of the particular partner and their prospective children. If either partner has a chronic condition or a history of some illness which might restrict their activity or affect child-bearing, this, too, must be communicated. Again, they may do well to consult their physician in order to be thoroughly informed as to the risks, the means of helping the afflicted partner and the limits which the condition may impose upon their relationship. Whatever the information may be, it is better to have it before marriage than to discover the painful facts afterwards. With time to think and time to talk, the couple can be expected to arrive at sound conclusions regarding these problems. Very few conditions need to be seriously considered as an obstacle to marriage. The most important thing is the quality of love which governs their attitudes and values. Where this is mature, they can learn to live with almost any medical problem.

More commonly, couples are concerned with the question of how much to reveal of their past as it concerns prior romantic or sexual experiences. Males are more apt to let it be known that they are "experienced" and it not infrequently happens that the girl prefers that they are, saying in substance, "I hope one of us knows what to do!" Because of the attitudes of most men and the special sensitivities of most girls, the latter are much more hesitant to admit any prior sexual experience. Whatever the reasons may be for the occurrence of previous sexual relations, it is the

author's opinion that there is no general *necessity* for
the confession thereof. There are private chapters in
the lives of all of us. Revealing them is not always
desirable and the mature couple respects this right of
privacy in each other. The mature person does not
"have" to know all. This is not to say that these matters cannot be discussed, but rather to indicate that
one does not have the right to inquire into the life of
the other. If confession or revelation occurs it should
only be because the confessor wishes to impart the
facts and face the consequences. The mature person
receiving this information will not feel threatened nor
cheated. He or she will bring love and understanding
to this sensitive situation and if, as a result, he be wiser
than he was, he need not also be sadder.

11. *Religious Problems*

In the course of establishing friendships and certainly
when a young couple contemplates engagement and
marriage, any religious differences present are of concern and quite properly should be faced by those
involved. Most people tend to believe that religious
affiliation is largely an accident of birth; that we had
little more to say in choosing our religion than we did
in choosing our parents and that we are "brought up"
in the faith of our parents rather than elect it from
free choice. Be that as it may, children are taught
religious attitudes, practices and beliefs and incidentally
a number of ideas and feelings regarding others who
worship differently or not at all. The result is not only
the establishment of a special set of theological concepts, but also of social attitudes. Inevitably the
growing child in the average household experiences

periods of religious doubts, some based on his inability
to grasp theological conflicts or reconcile them with
reality as experienced; some because of too little or
too much religious pressure; and some because traditional social attitudes and prejudices fostered in a
religious atmosphere are in conflict with their social
experiences. When marriage is contemplated, the
religious beliefs or doubts of both parties must be
examined.

Those who have investigated the results of inter-
marriage of religious faiths agree that this adds to the
problems most young couples face and that such
marriages seem to have a higher incidence of trouble
if not actually ending more frequently in the divorce
courts. It is not hard to find reasons for this and it
is not to my purpose to pursue these in detail. Neither
is it my purpose to argue the issues extensively. However, since these matters are significant experiences in
human life, they cannot be omitted entirely from our
consideration.

Today in America a variety of religious attitudes
having "social significance" prevail. Almost unique,
compared to any other country in the world, is our
socio-political attitude toward personal religious belief.
Just as some people equate sociology with socialism,
so do many equate atheism or agnosticism with com-
munism. This becomes painfully obvious in the false
syllogism of the modern witch-hunter: Communists
do not believe in God, you do not believe in God,
therefore, you are a Communist. It is un-American
to have religious doubts or not attend Church. The
rush of prominent ex-Communists to the protection
of orthodoxy should not be made a cause for great

rejoicing in the sanctuaries of our great cathedrals. Be that as it may, the presence of such public and official attitudes does not necessarily make for healthy or sincere religious belief.

Secondly, when "brotherhood" is publicly acclaimed and privately scorned or at best patronized, it is little wonder our young people either succumb to traditional prejudices or, in rebellion, too quickly turn away from their faiths. Intelligent young people are often appalled by the bigotry of their elders and yet must finally be the perpetuators thereof because of the enormous pressures brought to bear by their families, their groups and the public at large.

Religious differences which divide Christian from Jew, and Catholic from Protestant are to be reckoned with. Most clergymen earnestly believe that to marry outside one's Church is to invite trouble. This is supported by most families, no matter how unclear they may be regarding the nature of the differences of one Church from another. The roots of prejudice run deeply and often quite "liberal" persons who marry find critical periods in their marriages when their religious differences become bones of contention. This may be when Church attendance becomes a problem or when religious education for children must be discussed. It may emerge when other problems lead to a storm of recriminations in which cruel words emerge to reveal unhealthy attitudes. At times families keep the issue before the couple and loyalties are severely strained.

For most young people, these problems are too much to struggle against and all young couples whose religious backgrounds are different should carefully consider the possibilities. However, there are times when mature, intelligent young people of different faiths, nationality and color do fall in love, deeply and completely. They will be faced with harsh public opinion and with private doubts, but surely God must look with favor on those who love truly and who, in their love, fulfill His commandments best. Such marriages have worked and can work, though the way may often be hard.

It is certainly to be expected that these exceptional personalities will face these problems before committing themselves to an engagement, let alone to a marriage. Characteristically, they will search their own hearts to determine what they personally believe and then in frank deliberation will face each other; finding where there are similarities and differences. They will then attempt to evaluate the differences. If these can neither be reconciled nor compromised they will of necessity seriously consider termination of the relationship. This will not be likely to occur when the differences are within the same general religious institution, as for example, between the Methodist and Baptist within the larger Protestant body. However, when the differences derive from the divergent beliefs of Catholics, Protestants and Jews, they are much more difficult to resolve. In many such instances, conversion of one partner is often the only way out if the couple is to marry. When this is considered, it should not be done as an accommodation if there are serious religious feelings involved which may later be the basis of guilt and resentment.

It follows, then, that the more agreement there is on these issues, the less likelihood that they will be sources of trouble later. Hence, it follows that, in general, people will do better to marry within their own faiths. But, interfaith marriages are not by definition doomed to failure, nor do they of necessity corrupt the religious attitudes of such people as enter them. The mature personalities will be able to cope with the situation because they are religious in their attitude toward life if not in their church affiliation.

When at last the couple approaches the actual marriage, they will have made plans well in advance and in open consultation with the families involved. Oftentimes the latter wish to dictate the details of the wedding. If this is mutually acceptable to the couple, then there is no problem. However, the desires of the couple should be given consideration and if, as often happens, they do not wish a large formal wedding and reception, the social ambitions or "obligations" of the families should be waived. Oftentimes the money spent on such festivities could be used by the couple for better purposes and a small, family wedding can be more dignified and moving than some of the public spectacles that make the society pages.

With this, we conclude the discussion of growth and development prior to marriage and are now ready to see what maturity means in the conduct of that relationship. I would point out that growth will continue and that maturation is not static and we shall see in our study of marriage that time and circumstance continue to change us all, preparing us for the successive stages of life unto the very end.

CHAPTER III

MARRIED LIFE

1. *Adam and Eve*

As an introduction to our study of married life, I would like to dwell at some length on an analysis of the Adam and Eve story. Great literature has long been distinguished by the ability of its creators to communicate to the reader very penetrating insights into the personality of unique individuals and into universal characteristics of human nature. Myths and legends are also rich sources of material for clues to the meaning of complex but basic human qualities. The Bible, whatever one's personal belief regarding its origins, is likewise a repository of much wisdom regarding fundamental aspects of human motivations, needs and goals. Much has been made of the Adam and Eve story by theologians, with heavy emphasis on the sins and punishments involved in their lives. Much of Western civilization's treatment of sex and the role of women stems from the Judeo-Christian interpretation of this story. In more recent times, the interest of psychoanalysts and allied scholars have re-examined this and other ancient writings from another point of view. In these latter instances, the emphasis has been either on such things as sexual symbolism, incest taboo, the Oedipal conflict and the like, or upon comparison with similar myths and legends from other sources. In my own study of this section of the Book of Genesis,

I see first of all a very simple and beautiful story of growth and development, and secondly, a profound statement of the essential nature of marriage. Aided by the insights of psychoanalysis, I believe we may use this story as an object lesson and as a means of bridging the gap from the preceding section of this book to the one we are now beginning.

Chapter two of the Book of Genesis begins with the description of the first Sabbath and continues with the planting of the Garden of Eden. Verses 21 to 25 which close this chapter deal with the creation of Eve. Verses 24 and 25 are of particular significance: "Therefore shall a man leave his father and his mother and shall cleave unto his wife and they shall be one flesh. And they were both naked, the man and his wife, and were not ashamed."

In the passage just quoted, there are several things to note: (1) the mention of a father and mother, though none exist, (2) the prediction of future sexual union, though they had as yet no knowledge thereof, and (3) the abrupt reference to the fact that they were naked and without shame. To me, this is a statement of prediction of eventual sexual maturity out of a state of sexual innocence — the innocence of children, who find no shame in their nakedness. It is a prediction that there will be fathers and mothers who will produce children, who in turn will leave them and join with others, man and woman, and through their union produce more children. None of this can happen, of course, until they gain knowledge of these things and at this point in the story, Adam and Eve are but children psychosexually.

Chapter three introduces us to the Temptation and

so-called Fall of Man. We are re-introduced to the tree whose fruit it was forbidden to eat — the Tree of Knowledge. The serpent says, "For God doth know that in the day ye eat thereof, then your eyes shall be opened, and *ye shall be as God, knowing good and evil.*"

Only with learning can they achieve what was predicted and from the Tree of Knowledge they would learn to make value judgments to determine what was good and what was evil. More than that, they would learn to do that which their own Creator had done; namely, bring forth new life, made in their own image, of their own flesh. This is also a recognition of the universal conflict between parents (creators) and children, as the latter grow to maturity and gain knowledge of that which was previously the secret of the parents — the knowledge of sex and reproduction.

In the Biblical story and in actual life, we have long recognized the reluctance of parents to impart sexual knowledge to their children. In Western civilization, sex education was, until recent times, almost negligible and usually both inadequate and grossly distorted. It was cloaked in mystery and heavily burdened with guilty and painful fears. This did not prevent sexual experience, but it did place it in the category of animal lust and at best a necessary evil.

In primitive times, there was some justification for the apprehension of the elders concerning the coming of sexual maturity of the males. Among animals, the lusty young males, eager for sex and combat, strutted among the others and this was a signal to the older males of battles to come for the possession of any and all females, regardless of their family relationships.

This often meant death or isolation for the leader or family head. Incestuous matings were commonplace.

Primitive human social groups, being less powerful than the animals, could not have survived unless their own group unity could be more effectively preserved. To survive, they had to work together, under a group leader and the heads of family units who could not risk being seriously challenged, especially by youths eager for sex and battle. To preserve the family and group, it was then necessary to drain off the hostilities of the young men by diverting them to hunting and to combat with other groups. Control of sexual drives was gained through the establishment of rigid taboos against incest and by the arrangement of easy and early marriages with members of other families. In time, the injunctions against sex became increasingly restrictive, until, in fairly recent times any sexual act by a child (such as sexplay with himself or other children) would be looked upon with horror and bring with it the cruelest of threats and punishments. It was made even worse for girls who, because of interpretations of the Bible, were regarded as inherently sinful and therefore to be kept in complete ignorance of sex or at best to be taught to regard it as a loathsome duty. It is little wonder that fear, shame and revulsion were the common experiences of the bride, and that males in their ignorance of the real meaning of sex, sought to sow their wild oats elsewhere and were less than effective lovers at home.

To return to Adam and Eve, we are next concerned with their fate as a consequence of their eating the forbidden fruit. The usual interpretation made is that they were severely punished — and this, of course, has given generations of parents free license to punish their children for "sexual offenses." To me, it seems that the deeper meanings of the text go beyond the idea of punishment in the conventional sense. One cannot in justice punish someone for doing that which they were predestined to do. The story actually indicates that the Creator knew what they would do before they did, and that they, therefore, in their innocence, had no choice at all. The concept of their being punished was the product of the thinking of generations of much later time. I prefer to believe that the knowledge of good and evil which came from eating the forbidden fruit was the natural result of growing up. Having moved on through the stages of infancy and childhood, as we described them earlier, they learned things; and what they learned was that life can be bitter as well as sweet, full of pain and joy, and always a mystery of somewhat awesome and terrifying proportions. They learned that they must work and often suffer to survive, but that they could also rest and know the wonders of love, ecstasy and creativity. They learned that things need not be good nor evil in themselves, but that how they used them may be the crucial determinant. This is most certainly true of sex, and to indict it as inherently evil is to malign the essence of life and its Creator.

The Adam and Eve story is a profound declaration of the nature of life as man and woman can know it — that for all the hardships and the awareness of their quite earthly existence, they can with knowledge yet be as Gods. For this, we endure the travail. We endure it because we are capable of love. Without love there is only loneliness and terror. Self-love is not enough. As the story predicted, "and (he) shall cleave unto his wife; and they shall be one flesh."

I have occasionally used the word "ecstasy" in connection with sexual experience, especially as it applies to the relationship of man and wife. It literally means "to stand outside." As it refers to emotional states, it means to stand outside one's self, to lose one's self. This actually applies to religious as well as sexual ecstasy and implies an abandonment of self to union with something outside one's self. In the light of the Biblical text, our forebears must have early recognized the powerful and far-reaching significance of the sexual relationship, ranging as it can from a momentary surge of animal lust to an act of love expressing our highest capacities for God-like existence. In this context, I would next refer to the first verse of Chapter four in Genesis: "and Adam *knew* Eve his wife; and she conceived and bore Cain." The text does not say they had intercourse, or as the courts say, that he had carnal knowledge of her. The simple and beautiful statement is made that Adam *knew* his wife, and this is to me a most profound expression of the essential substance of marriage. What did Adam "know"? He knew Eve as a human being, as a woman. He knew her in their sharing of joy and sorrow. He knew her moods and needs, as she knew his. He knew her secret ways, the delights of her body and the inner workings of her heart and mind. He knew, too, that he was an imperfect creature, but yet acceptable to her as she was to him. Each in their imperfection and incompleteness became something better and more complete in each other. The abandonment of self to union with the other in the totality of their life is epitomized in the ecstatic climax of the sexual embrace when they become as one flesh, merging with each other and the full-flowing stream of life. Thus it is, in the story of the first man and woman, that we can now see the story of life; from birth, through childhood to the full flowering of mature love that comes with experience, knowledge and understanding. As it was then, so can it be now for those who will learn and work.

With this in mind, let us now continue our exposition of our subject; moving on to observe the meaning of maturity in a marriage, from the time of the honeymoon until "death do us part."

2. *The Honeymoon*

I have already laid much stress on courtship as a time in which the couple gets to "know" each other. There remains much to be learned — much to know. But all knowledge is a preparation for further knowledge; leading us to ever new and deeper understanding of ourselves and others. Courtship has been but a beginning step on the threshold of rich new experiences.

Traditionally, the honeymoon has been given to the young couple to provide them privacy during their first days and nights as husband and wife. Isolation from friends and family affords freedom from embarrassment and teasing and the necessity for having to hide emotions occasioned by either joy or disappointment. The initiation to married life is quite properly a private affair and is best conducted in distant surroundings with freedom from work and routine obligations.   It should be a holiday, in the dual meaning the term connotes — of both fun and holiness, an observation of a joyous sacred rite.

It would be foolish to believe that all the potentials for sexual experience would or could be explored and fulfilled within the period of the honeymoon.   It is theoretically possible that the couple could mechanically perform all the physical acts listed in the more encyclopedic sex manuals, but this is not the real goal.   The tests of love are yet to come.   They have not "lived" together in any real sense.   Those who would make of the honeymoon a display of their sexual sophistication and erotic knowledge are doomed to disappointment, though the price may not be paid until a much later time.   The immature seek exciting self-gratifications and are apt to overlook the offenses they have committed against the sensitivities and needs of the mate.   The mature couple realizes that this is a beginning for each of them and their healthy desires are tempered with a tenderness and control which permits the gradual shedding of restraint and a build-up of emotion essential for genuine satisfaction.

So often it happens that the honeymoon comes as a climax to rather exhausting preparations.   It would be too much to expect that excitement, fatigue and even anxiety would not be present when at last the couple is alone.   Anticipating this may enable them to manage the prenuptials and ceremony as to permit departure during the day and with some freedom from fatigue.   It is not, of course, impossible nor undesirable that under less favorable circumstances they would abstain from intercourse the first night.   One reason for this is that fatigue and the other emotions conflict with sexual feelings, and since males and females differ in their response patterns to sexual stimulation, it would be very unlikely that the couple would experience a climax of mutual satisfaction. With many couples, there is the belief that intercourse is the primary objective of the first night of the honeymoon. Consequently, ready or not, the relationship takes place. The usual result is that the male achieves satisfaction quickly and the bride is left aroused, but unfulfilled. This usually leads to some sense of guilt and inadequacy on the part of the male, who tries to pass it off and usually falls promptly to sleep. The woman is tense, restless, and probably both resentful and at the same time concerned as to her own adequacy.

Actually, in the final analysis, it is not really just a question of simultaneity of climax that is involved, but of attitudes as well. The approach is important, and at this time even more important than the result. The mature couple knows that not *every* sexual relationship will be equally satisfying to both partners, but that the relationship is asked for or given as an act of love (not lust alone) is the important thing. In those instances where the bride is yet a virgin, and particularly if medical examination has revealed the presence of an intact hymen, there will be an element of fear as well as desire. The husband must appreciate this, have some knowledge of the nature of the mechanical problem involved and be able to exploit her natural desire in order to overcome her fear. This is less easy to accomplish if both are worn out from the festivities preceding the wedding or if they are unprepared for the possibilities of that circumstance. They must also recognize that they have a lifetime ahead of them, not just one night. The general principles stated in the first part of this book, regarding lovemaking now apply. For those wishing more technical information they may find the references in the bibliography useful.

The honeymoon is not only a time for sexuality, but also a time for fun and relaxation prior to a life of homemaking and bread-winning. It is a time for seeing sights, for mutually desired indulgences and for learning how to share the intimacies of bathroom and living room as well as bedroom. Little personal habits never recognized before now show up which may delight or disappoint one or the other of them. Our imperfections stand out under different circumstances and the honeymoon may bring to light certain ones never before seen. The tactful, but direct, facing of these may seem to rob the honeymoon of some of its lustre, but may go a long way toward setting a healthy pattern of communication for the future. It would be pointless to attempt to catalogue the little things which might crop up to annoy one of them, but it is important that the offended party recognize the offense and try to cope with it directly. Mature newlyweds are more likely to accept suggestions than those who are not. The latter are more apt to be hurt or angry and visualize the future as one long dreary routine of "constructive criticism."

I would conclude this chapter with one last observation of the sexual aspect of the honeymoon and beyond. However much I have pictured the sexual union as a profound ecstatic experience, I would hasten to add that sex should also involve an element of fun and lightness of heart. We have already seen that the preliminary love-making of adult partners is in a large sense a recapitulation of childhood sexual discovery and play. In the marital relationship, this affords not only an approach to intercourse, but the means of recapturing the forbidden delights of earlier times without guilt or fear of discovery. In a sense, they begin as Adam and Eve, who in their innocence knew no shame in their nakedness.

3. *After Eden — The Early Years*

With the return from the honeymoon, the couple settles down to the earnest business of being not only young lovers, but homemakers and responsible citizens. Now they will begin to learn what living together means. A wide range of circumstances will serve to test the adjustment capacities of each of them. The very fact of being together so much, under the scrutiny of family, society and their own self-awareness, may make for restlessness, boredom and a feeling of being imprisoned. Not infrequently, personal habits and mannerisms once regarded as cute or distinguishing become sources of irritation through constant repetition. Expectations and demands come in conflict, feelings get hurt and tempers may spill over without much provocation. Previously concealed doubts about the partner now obtrude and unwelcome misgivings about life and love cast shadows over the relationship. Budget problems, social obligations, differences in taste regarding clothes, food and choice of friends loom large upon the scene. To one degree or another these are the kinds of things which appear in the course of every marriage. The natural friction of living together throws off sparks until the couple can fit to themselves as a smoothly running unit. Too often the sparks are interpreted as indicators of failures and signs that the marriage was a horrible mistake. When this occurs, self-interest begins to dominate the adjustment (defense) techniques. Arguments may be as bitter as they are pointless, because by this time, each is more concerned with winning than with settling it. I do not intend to discuss in detail the special and serious problems which may arise in individual cases. What I wish to communicate is recognition of the fact that all couples have "problems" and that the real issue is how they cope with them. The outcome is a function of the level of maturity of the partners. It is this which enables them to acknowledge their differences and find the means of adjustment which will reduce their power to cause trouble. While it is true that immature individuals create more problems than others, this does not mean that the latter have no problems nor that the former cannot be helped. As long as we are willing to learn, we can change.

What is it that distinguishes the mature couple during the early years of marriage? I believe there are at least two major characteristics which mark their adjustment capacities; (1) *an ability to regard marriage as a 60-60 proposition,* and (2) *the ability to communicate effectively.*

Regarding the first of these, I would hasten to point out that that was no typographical error — 60-60 is correct. Too many couples subscribe to a 50-50 division of labor, as if quite willing to meet their partners half-way. What generally happens is that the line gets drawn not only very sharply, but usually somewhere short of half-way, since self-interest tends to define the individual's very personal concept of "half-way." Fifty-fifty may work well in some business partnerships, but not in marriage. In a 60-60 relationship, each member is willing to go more than half-way and this is a matter of heart, not of weights and measures. In practice, it means making concessions and giving indulgences without being solicited for such. It means seeing things in such perspective that a minor personal sacrifice is not regarded as an irreparable loss of face or status. It means appreciating that what one has and is working towards is of far greater value than what one might gain in winning a battle.

The second item, effective communication, is also extremely important. What should be "communicated"? The answer to this is "everything." By answering thus, we de-limit the range of communicable subject matter and include not only the negative or painful things, but also the positive things which are the sweet-meats of love.

The mature couple freely exchanges sentiments, affectionate words and declarations of love. There is something wrong if a man or woman in the privacy of their home find themselves too embarrassed to say simply "I love you." How often have I heard men say "she knows I love her!", and then have the wife say, "yes, but it would be nice to hear it once in a while." It is not necessary that the individuals concerned recite love-poems or make elaborate speeches. Words of praise for little things well done are always welcome to both parties as evidence that their efforts are not just taken for granted. In more intimate situations, words of endearment and expressions of pleasure enhance the love-making by fanning the flames, not only of desire, but of desire to please. In the more prosaic atmosphere of the daily stint, everyone experiences some fatigue, frustration and irritation, so that by the end of the day we long for pleasant diversion or rest. The wife would be grateful if she could be given respite from her chores by a thoughtful and cheerful husband. He, in turn, enters the house, hopeful that his wife will look pretty, give him affection, and in recognition of his "hard day at the office," wait upon him with little indulgences. The situation as they greet each other constitutes one of the minor dramas of everyday life. The mature couple sees the position each occupies in this archetypical domestic mise-en-scene and, appreciating the humor therein, joins forces to lighten the burdens each bears. The less mature see only their own sides and in a rush of self-pity fall into those pointless arguments which no one wins.

However difficult it may be for some people to express positive feelings or confront potentially disruptive situations with humor, it is apparently quite easy for most people to express resentment and hostility. The picture of the nagging wife and her hen-pecked husband is but a caricature of what exists all too often. An equally unhappy portrait is that of the male, who by virtue of his role of breadwinner, assumes that his wife is a servant to his needs and forces his will upon her. There is no lack of communication in these situations. However, *what* is communicated and *how*, is of great importance. How often have I heard people complain that they cannot "talk" to their mates without an argument or silent dismissal. For mature couples, there is a time for thinking and a time for talking. The former is the individual's method of examining the situation before bringing it to the attention of the mate. It allows time for digestion and reflection, and formulation of questions. When the time for talking comes, the subject in question is brought up when there is privacy and sufficient freedom from other distractions to permit adequate discussion. The presenting partner is able to approach the topic with confidence and the other one to accept it without anxiety because each one is prepared to respect the other and acknowledge that "we" have a problem. They are also strengthened by the knowledge that in facing their problems in this manner, they will not only arrive at a solution but probably feel closer than ever. It is only in such an atmosphere that profitable discussion can take place.

The conduct of these discussions is neither academic nor necessarily a chatty little venture in constructive criticism. They may be highly emotional and at times bitter, but there are still important differences between these episodes and the "arguments" mentioned elsewhere. First of all, they follow some period of thinking by the offended partner, and secondly, the other partner is capable of hearing the mate out before responding. Each knows that feelings must be honestly and completely discharged and each is prepared to face the possibility of being in the wrong. Once the grievances are ventilated, they can be faced objectively and the means of redress or solution can be explored. The solutions, like the grievances, are sought in terms of "what can *we* do about it?"

The foregoing might suggest that such a couple lets things pile up until a big explosion is imminent and that between times, they exude charm and delicate manners. This is most certainly not true. With this couple, little things are not likely to be made big issues, and in daily contacts they are able to express themselves quite freely. The "big problems" which may require a real session are usually complex and not readily recognizable at first glance. They often involve much more than a single incident to which one of them reacts adversely. They are usually matters which have slowly crept into the situation and undramatically but effectively produce a change in the relationship. These things may stem from seeming shifts in attitudes and values as they reflect from use of leisure time, choice of friends, management of financial matters, attitudes towards work or the home or even the mate. Sometimes the "problems" appear more circumscribed, but rather delicate; such as the over-use of creams and salves (beauty-aids) by the wife at bedtime, or failure of the husband to be reasonably clean and smooth-shaven at bedtime (and yet eager for sexual relations).

Whatever the cause of the disharmony, the subject will be brought up and thoroughly explored. Discussion continues, all night if necessary, not to find a winner or a loser, but to find a solution acceptable to both sides. The ability to admit error is very important and for mature people constitutes not so much a defeat as a gain in knowledge and added respect for one's mate and one's self.

Just as the privacy of the bedroom is the logical and practical place for intimacy and sexual relationships, so, too, is it a good place to settle grievances and quarrels. In the quiet of the night, free from distractions and in close contact with the body of one's mate, it is much easier to be magnanimous and a lot harder to act out our feelings in the dramatic posturing likely to be demonstrated in the living room. Then, when at last, the issues are settled, the resurgence of love and desire attendant upon the relief from painful feelings, floods the couple and the reunion of spirit and flesh teaches us most effectively the deeper meanings of love and sex. No casual sexual "affair" can ever offer such experience.

4. *Children*

It goes without saying that most couples want children and take it for granted that in accepting marriage, they will in time establish a family group. During the engagement period, most couples discuss this subject; each one eagerly expressing anticipation, but with the young mother-to-be speaking of "dozens of babies" and the young man gulping uncertainly at this challenge to his earning power and virility. At any event, they do plan to have children and their equally eager parents keep a watch for the signs of pregnancy.

Behind this commonplace but wonderful state are some very real "facts of life" to consider. Nature, as viewed by some, is a vast dynamic system of forces organized to fulfill specific functions and ends. They mistake the scientist's use of such a term as "natural law" to indicate the existence of fixed, eternal and goal-directed operations of the forces of nature inherent in the very substance of things. This idea, long held by traditional speculative philosophy and theology, inevitably gave rise to a number of beliefs and attitudes which have blinded us to some facts which, if acknowledged, would seriously challenge some highly cherished beliefs. Among these is the main assumption that the female (human and animal) is endowed with a special instinct called "mother love," that in the profligate fecundity of plants, beasts and humans, we have evidence of a desire for parenthood and that the manifest concern of a mother for her child is eloquent proof of the existence of that instinct.

However poetic the vision and moralistic the biology, there is little scientific validity for such conclusions. This is not to deny the intense devotion and self-sacrifice of which individual mothers are capable, but for the sake of honesty, let us recognize that such qualities are neither universal (for all mothers) nor necessarily continuous (in any one mother). Some animals will eat their young unless quickly separated from them. Others ignore their offspring, allowing them to shift for themselves soon after weaning. Among humans, the patterns of mothering differ in different cultures and within the same culture there will be wide-ranging differences from one family to another. As a matter of fact, the more complex the culture (civilized?) the less uniform and stable are the patterns.

Those of us whose work brings us into contact with these problems in clinical situations have had to recognize that many women (and men, also) face pregnancy, delivery and child rearing with at least mixed emotions, if not with obvious anxiety, resentment and loathing. Furthermore, many a young mother has seemingly wanted children, yet unconsciously feared and hated them. This may become evident with the first pregnancy and take origin in deeply hidden conflicts which arose in their own childhood. It may come with the fourth or fifth child, in families where the physical and economic strain and the attitude of her mate has robbed the woman of any capacity for joy and fulfillment in the dignified and effective conduct of her role as wife and mother. In some families children are produced largely to fulfill the ego-needs of the male. In others, they are seen as sources of support in the latter years of the parents' lives. In still others, the children become the agencies for the expression of the frustrated ambitions of the parents or for emotional satisfactions which failed to develop between the parents. In short, when viewed objectively, we find ourselves once again confronted by a now familiar thesis — the quality of mothering is a function of the level of maturity of the mother — not of an instinct which automatically endows her with all the graces, virtues and depth of feeling which can adorn her sex. The same is also true of fathers, though by virtue of their different biological and social roles, not as much is expected of them. It may well be that the popular belief in an "instinctive mother love" is a myth created largely by men to glorify and at the same time dominate the female by imposing on her an obligatory attitude which she would be ashamed to deny. Man's own awe of life and of the function of the female undoubtedly has contributed to this situation — as if the mysterious power ascribed to her because of her role in reproduction evoked conflicting emotions in the male, leading him to use his superior strength to dominate her and at the same time necessitating that he revere her. Thus, the female became an imprisoned Goddess. Modern woman, despite her seeming gains as in individual in the culture, is still expected to be something more than human in her role as mother and this is attributed to her natural devotion, wisdom and skill in

her relationship to her children. Our naiveté is really
quite astonishing. As individuals, we are expected,
even commanded, to regard our own mothers as completely wonderful creatures, incapable of error or sin.
We censor any man or woman who is not "good to his
mother," but we reserve the right to recognize that the
other person's mother may be mean, possessive, cruel,
foolish or plainly stupid. The height of this absurdity
is reached on "Mother's Day," and God help the man
or woman who forgets to make proper declaration of
his undying gratitude to the woman who bore him or
her. Aided and abetted by the hucksters and mer-
chants this special day has become a Freudian Circus,
complete with all the trappings for a public orgy of
expiation and immolation.

Having spoken thus, let me hasten to point out that
this in no way implies that the behavioral scientist is
either cynical or censorious in his basic attitude toward
mankind in general or women in particular. In de-
nouncing falsehood and hypocrisy, there is the sincere
desire to render real respect and homage to those who
merit it. In destroying the idea that all mothers are
perfect by reason of an instinct, we restore not merely
a realistic appraisal of womankind, but what is more
important, more adequately appreciate those women
who do in fact approach the ideal through hard work
and the deliberate effort to grow in their roles. If we,
therefore, recognize that all mothers are neither created
equal nor make equal effort to be good mothers, we can
arrive at a better understanding and appreciation of
those who do succeed, and of how to help others to do
better. If modern psychology seems to have spent
much time kicking mother off her pedestal, let us real-

ize that this was actually for the purpose of establishing a real basis for respect and not a mythical one.

If, as we have said, the quality of mothering is a function of the level of maturity of the individual, then let us examine the so-called mature woman (and her mate) in her relationship to her offspring.

If the evolution of man has brought with it not only increased knowledge and capacity to learn, it has also awakened in him a more poignant awareness of the vastness of his universe and a pervasive anxiety about his ultimate end. Religion has in part satisfied and eased his fears by promise of eternal life beyond the grave. Yet, deep within us is a desire for some earth-bound extension of self, perpetuating our physical being in living flesh. In the act of love, uniting man and woman, the cycle of life, as we are able to see it, is maintained. However commonplace the occurrence, the phenomena of conception, gestation, and birth remain a never-ending source of profound experience for most of us. In beholding one's newborn child, who has not felt a surge of emotion in the realization that "this is of my flesh and blood," in this infant is my tie with immortality? For the woman there comes a sense of fitness and fulfillment in the sensations from her body that signal the presence of a new life within her. If there be pain in the effort of delivery, there is also joy and triumph, and when, with the rush of milk to her breasts, she gives of her body once more, being, in the larger sense, becomes a fact. The capacity to see and feel beyond the discomfort and the pain, to be at one with one's self, mate, child and with life, is to come as close to Godliness as we can know it. It is this which the mature woman is prepared to comprehend.

With the passage of time and with the growth of the child come the privileges of teaching, of shaping the behavior patterns and discovering the new modes of love that can come with parent-child relationships. The delight to be found in the child's pleased gurgles, in its first words and first steps, well compensate for the diapers, colic and interrupted sleep. Our couple anticipates the common sources of frustration and irritation attendant to the presence of a baby, and are therefore forearmed. Because *they* are mature, the narcissism of the baby is no threat or serious imposition. They know that the primary obligations go from parent to child and they neither demand nor expect gratitude or repayment. They are ready to share the chores and in times of difficulty with the infant, divide duties so as to give each other respite. They do not blame the baby for crying and if they regret the loss of sleep or imposition on their privacy they temper it with humor or calm resignation. They strive to provide an atmosphere of warmth and stability, trust and confidence, and by their own obvious behavior, present a model of marriage which will influence the child positively in his own search for love-objects.

As the child develops motor and speech skills and moves out into the uncertain society of school and neighborhood, he remains confident in the familiar and protective stability of home. His normal curiosity and activity needs are encouraged, but limits are firmly set by his parents who realize that love is not enough to guide children. Our couple appreciates the necessity for establishing solid boundaries appropriate to the age of the child. They can maintain these in the face of the child's demands and the inconsistencies of their neighbors. They will listen to reasonable arguments, but not be unduly influenced by the popular (if often erroneous) standards of nearby families. They will always try to do what is best in the long run for their child, even if it is not the easiest way. This will often mean denying to the child the questionable indulgences other families provide their children — they know that just because nearby Johnny or Mary gets to do certain things does not make it right or proper for their child.

All this could, of course, harden into an over-protective and too restrictive program, but it need not be such. It is still possible to enable the child to have a full and active life. That which is denied him will be but a relatively small portion of his daily life and in many instances his parents will furnish substitute activities which will be acceptable to the child. The mature parents, in contrast to those of lesser stature, see in their relationship with their children an opportunity to recapture some of the adventure of discovery of the world as they assist them in their learning experiences. From the days of the first blocks and picture-books, through stages of doll-families and construction toys, on into the world of facts and fantasies as revealed in books, music and excursions, parents relive much of the delights of the past, with the added pleasure of leading their own children to a richer use of their senses in perceiving the world around them. The difficulty lies in pacing this to the child's needs and at the same time fitting it all into our busy schedules. Furthermore, we are apt to be frustrated when our efforts seem unappreciated and our offspring do not quite play the game. They often grow restive and bored and they sometimes may seem even a little dumb as they fail to grasp our revelations. And often, just when we are ready to devote time to them, they want to do other things. Parents need time and experience in which to learn their trade and they need not despair if at times, their efforts seem to go unrewarded. If they create a general atmosphere that encourages questioning and make themselves interested in the world of the child, they will be pleasantly surprised at the results gained with actually little time out from other things. Oftentimes, especially for fathers, five or ten minutes of deliberate attention in an evening is sufficiently reassuring to a youngster so that later when more serious questions arise in his mind, he will not hesitate to turn to his parents for guidance. Beyond this, fathers must decide what is of most importance to them — the golf game or an afternoon with the family — a TV program or half an hour working with junior at his erector set — an hour by himself or an hour reading to the children. There is room for all these things if we are willing to share our lives with others, but we shall have to decide what we want and know we cannot have everything. We try to teach this to a child, but may forget it when it comes to ourselves.

In view of our previous discussion of infantile and childhood sexual feelings, we may now turn our attention to a consideration of how the mature parents assist their children in the acquisition of both knowledge and attitudes concerning the whole domain of love and sex.

First of all, the parents, by their own conduct, establish an atmosphere within the home which provides for healthy acceptance of affection and communication of feelings and freedom from false modesty or hesitancy to ask questions. Bathing and toilet functions are not hidden. Affection is freely expressed by all members of the family and the children not only share in this, but observe the obvious pleasure of the parents in their own relationship. Naturally, the parents do not engage in sexual intimacies before the children, nor do they make suggestive or veiled remarks which might puzzle them. If, in their own conversations, they should use words or ideas which the children do not understand and which provoke questions from the child, they will answer the question in terms understandable to him.

This leads us to a second consideration. All questions a child asks will be answered, and answered honestly, regardless of subject matter. If the parent does not know the answer, he or she will admit it and offer to try to find one. A good basic rule for parents is to answer the questions of a child briefly, precisely and unencumbered by elaborate explanations or moralizations. There is no need to go beyond the scope of the child's question since his frame of reference and his need at that point is focused on his single question. He may follow this up with another question, in which case he gets an answer, or he may go for days or months until, having digested the newly acquired knowledge, he is ready to go on to a next step. In their response to questions, parents will use proper terms for the functions or organs under consideration and not employ cute euphemisms which may only confuse the child. Baby is not carried in mommy's tummy; that is where food goes when we eat. Baby is carried in a special place called the uterus. Little Johnny has a penis, not a wee-wee. And little Mary has labia, a clitoris and a vagina. In most instances, the sequence of questions which arise in a child's mind evolve in a pretty logical and progressive manner so that he gradually acquires an ever enlarging and more detailed picture of sexuality.

As the child gains knowledge, the parents will naturally realize that the neighbor's children may have less of such knowledge or even different ideas and attitudes toward sex. They may be a cause of some concern; the parents wondering what their child will do with his knowledge and how he will cope with a world outside the home that may view things quite differently than they. The mature parents are able to show their child that certain things can be done at home which are not done elsewhere and that certain impluses are to be restrained because they are proper only under rather special conditions. Thus, it is all right to run around one's house without clothes, but not on the street. And one does not examine the bodies of one's friends or neighbors. These are forbidden, not because they are inherently evil, but simply because society's rules are against them and because these are special experiences to be confined to one's home or to later relationships with the person one loves as an adult. As these "why" questions arise, the parents try to give realistic reasons for the "do's" and "don'ts" of behavior; reasons based upon the meaning of the acts in question, the meaning of responsibility for the consequence of one's actions and the need to be able to control one's impulses so that they may not trespass on the rights of others nor lead the individual into behavioral habits which limit his or her progress to maturity. Self discipline is taught as a means of self development in the ability to tolerate frustration and delay gratifications during the search for deeper and more enduring relationships.

Finally, if the children can trust their parents, the chances are the parents can trust their children. When the time for testing comes, the mature parents know that their children will face temptations and that no amount of continuous lecturing or supervision can control the situation. They know that anyone can make a mistake, but they at least can take some measure of comfort in the knowledge that they prepared their children to meet life honestly and that if trouble comes, the children will feel secure in facing both it and their parents and be ready for the consequences.

This brings us to a crucial point in the whole discussion of parent-child relationships. So many parents have become almost pathologically over-concerned about doing "the right thing" in bringing up children. Much of this has been due to the influence of misguided professionals who have frightened the public with ominous predictions of neurosis or worse if the parents do not rigorously observe their special brand of "child psychology." Nothing could be more unnatural than raising a child by the book. Total confusion finally reigns when a group of mothers meet, each of whom uses a different book.

Our couple will not be above reading books, but they can absorb and digest information and integrate it into general attitudes rather than pieces of dogma. More important, they know that what is needed for the child is an atmosphere, a proper soil to grow in, rather than a rigid set of rules. This atmosphere starts with the attitudes the parents have for each other and the example they set for the child. The obvious evidence of mutual respect, consideration, tenderness and devotion demonstrated by the parents is not overlooked by the child, and when he sees that he is free to share in this, he cannot but hold his parents and his home in highest esteem.

Above all, the parents practice what they preach! If they believe in honesty, they are honest. They are not ashamed to live by their standards even if this means being a bit different than the crowd. They do not demand observance of the letter of the law by their children and then brag of how much they drank, how fast they drove, and how they padded an expense account or tax return. They know, too, that the values they live by are not acquired by intuition. They must be taught by word and deed to the young. This does not involve formal lecturing, but instead, by being good examples and taking advantage of situations which arise in daily life to teach the child the "whys and wherefores" which form the bases for value-judgments governing behavior.

To do this effectively, the services of *both* parents are needed. Obviously, by the very nature of our society, the husband has less direct contact with the children than does the mother. This does not mean that Dad should be excused from all responsibility other than financial or legislative. Too many fathers seem to regard their function in the family in these terms. Many fathers feel that because they are bread-winners, time away from the job should be leisure time in which they can rest or play before returning to work. Rest and play is important, but not only for fathers. Mother's work is often a 24-hour per day

proposition, in which she is at the beck and call of the
children, the household tasks and, in the evening, her
husband. Our couple takes full cognizance of this
situation and efforts are made to provide more equit-
able distribution of labors and responsibility. They
know that shared work provides more leisure time for
everybody and they contrive to establish routines of
mutual assistance which will get the work more quickly
done and free all of them for recreational pursuits.
No one is an object of special indulgence. Everyone
has something to do. Privileges are earned and good
work is rewarded — this applies to parents as well as
children.

In brief, the early years involve adjustment to basic-
ally new sets of experiences. These include the general problem of living with someone else in a total
relationship of co-equality and mutual inter-depend-
ency. Restrictions on personal freedom and increasing
responsibilities stir up reactions rooted in the egocentrism of earlier days, but the mature person is
aware of what he has gained by marriage and more
easily accepts the necessity for relinquishing the prerogatives of his pre-marital life.

In addition to this general situation, the early years
bring other, more specific and new experiences. These
include the qualitative and quantitative changes in
sexual activity that stem from the simple fact of living
continuously together as husband and wife; adjusting
needs and desires to the total complex of married life.
This is as we have seen, more than a matter of an
exercising of "legal" rights or exploitation of opportunity for frequent sexual intercourse. Other "new"
experiences include pregnancy, birth and child-rearing.

There is also the matter of establishing household routines, social relationships and relationships with in-laws. These and others constantly challenge the young couple, confronting them with unfamiliar demands and provoking emotional reactions often shocking to both of them. The mature couple acknowledges their inexperience and recovers more quickly from lapses into less mature behavior. Together they seek the means to cope with the "new" and gain more adequate understanding of both the situation and of themselves.

5. *The Middle Years*

If the problems of "the early years" center about the adjustment to new experiences, the "middle years" test us in rather different ways. This does not mean that we reach a time when nothing new happens to us. In that connection, I am quite content with the apt observation of Heraclitus, that "no man can step twice in the same river." However, we do recognize that there are periods in the lives of all of us when rather extensive changes occur in our individual psychobiologic states and in the kinds of demands made upon us by our environment. Just as puberty and adolescence constitutes such a period, so, too, have the early years of marriage. The middle years present us with quite different conditions and it is now time that we examine them.

In each period of life, however arbitrary the time boundaries may be, there are special problems by virtue of our particular systems of needs and capacities, and the demands made upon us by family, friends, job and community. We have seen how growth and

experience prepares us well or not for the particular
functions we are called upon to serve in the successive stages of our journey. A marriage, too, may be
said to demand different things of us at different times.
In this case, however, the conditions which give rise
to problems are often very subtly manifested and
usually involve things which begin within each of us
rather than as external circumstances which force
themselves upon us. Naturally, there will be changes
in the environment to which we all react, but the
alterations within ourselves are of singular importance
as determining factors in the over-all outcome.

The middle years may be said to extend roughly
from the tenth to twentieth year of marriage. Beyond
this temporal boundary, we may qualify this concept of
"the middle years" as that period when the oldest
child is on the threshold of puberty and the parents
are beginning to "feel their age." From family to
family, this will vary depending upon the parents' own
chronological ages, the number of children and their
special problems.

This is the period when the offspring are moving
through that state of mind and body called adolescence,
in which they are neither children nor adults and often
quite beyond our comprehension. It is also a period
when we seem to have caught up with our futures.
All life seemed to be devoted to getting ready for
a job and a family. Suddenly, we find that we have
these things and, perhaps for the first time, we begin
to cast backward glances at what now appears to be
the distant past. The children in their teens remind
us a bit too sharply of our own lost youth. Their
awkward, jet-propelled striving for sophistication, ad-

venture, popularity and knowledge leave us a little breathless and if at times exasperated, a bit nostalgic. Men become more conscious of their waistlines and women search in the mirror for tell-tale evidences of the seeming ravages of time. We find ourselves subject to aches and pains and other physical distresses which somehow seem more ominous. Dieting, keeping in shape and in good health become minor preoccupations. The loss or greying of hair is watched with some apprehension and feeble jests. It is in this period, too, that we are more conscious of the illness or death of contemporaries and perhaps we note the signs of age in parents and collateral elders. It is a time, too, when we question the goals we once set so optimistically and confidently. The job or profession has become routinized and perhaps the husband sees the economic ceiling has been reached. The wife looks at the repetitive task of housekeeping with less than eager delight and wonders, when she sees the slick fashion magazines, if she really missed her calling.

All in all, as it is a time of change for the children (into adulthood), it is a time of change for the parents, too, but where for the youngsters it is a time of hope and lust for life, it may well be a time of monotony and quiet despair for the unprepared parents. Here, indeed, is a crucial period and how we handle it may well determine the character of our lives for years to come.

There was a time when the age of forty meant "getting old" — or at least older in an undesirable sense. The statistics of the insurance companies gave some mathematical validity to an established attitude of mind. Today, with life expectancy extended considerably and

with the probability of even more years to be added
to that statistic for the future of many, things have
gotten even more complicated. However much we
cling to life and wish to stay the day of conclusion,
many face the long road of later years with fear and
uncertainty, and it is in the middle years that this
begins.

For many, there is tension, restlessness, boredom and
a kind of frantic effort to recapture or hold the evidence
of an eternal youthfulness. They play too hard and
sometimes work too hard. Every possible device is
employed to enhance the illusions of youthful vitality
and outlook. To see this at its pathetic worst, watch
them at play, on the golf course, at the card tables,
in their clubs or favorite bars, at conventions and
lodge meetings, on trips or vacations and at parties.
Hear the too hearty laugh and the shopworn boasts of
athletic or sexual power. Observe the empty gallan-
tries and flirtations, the caricaturized portrayal of more
youthful roles, and too often, the "affairs" or "tradesies"
of the pseudosophisticates. Here at play is the middle
year male and female, who never quite grew up and
who face with dread a future they cannot comprehend.
The pursuit of pleasure and economic security takes
on a rather desperate quality and one is reminded of
T. S. Eliot's "hollow men," who when the end comes,
will go out "not with a bang, but a whimper."

However overdrawn this portrait may be, it is but a
reflection of all of us from a representative few. None
of us escape entirely, but what might we find in the
lives of those who are able to avoid the more destructive effects of this insidious disorder? What does maturity afford at this time of life? A number of things

stand out, and as we might expect, they, too, take origin in what has preceded them in the pattern of family life already established.

First, in their relationship with their children, there is evidence of free-flowing communication. Differences of opinions and arguments occur, but in the final moments, the Right prevails. The parents will listen to reason, but if they are certain in their own judgment that they must enforce their rule, they will, and it is accepted. We also note that the children will bring questions to these parents and feel confident that they will receive attentive and honest consideration. School problems, personal problems, all are grist for the mill of family discussion. At the same time, privacy and independent thought is also respected. The parents want to know what the children do and where they spend time, but there is no insistence on "telling mother everything," no attempt by parents to be big sisters or brothers, and no spying. Mutual respect is evident and when the going gets rough the children are confident in their parents' love and judgment. For the parents, however hectic the times may often be, there is a quiet pride in the growth and maturation of their young, and when occasionally the teen-age boy or girl is impulsively affectionate or they bring their problems with trust to Mom or Dad, the cup of life is sweet indeed.

The second characteristic of our couple in these middle years is to be found in *their relationship with each other.* It is in these years that they have come to appreciate the fullness of their love. They have learned much about each other and ironed out most of their differences. In their case, familiarity breeds not contempt, but stability and security. They like each other's company and have established a wide range of mutual interests while at the same time respecting the individual interests of each. There is trust and confidence which leaves no room for doubt and jealousy. When questions do arise, they are not afraid to face them or each other. The art of compromise has been well-developed and they do not begrudge the concessions that must be made. Even in their sex life, they find new depths and dimensions of feeling. If the demands of the flesh are less imperative and urgent than before, they are all the more sensitive to the reactions of the partner; filling each with wonder and delight that the same act can continuously be as if beauty and passion were discovered anew. The aftermath of intercourse finds them clinging together, the tender words of love yet upon their lips as sleep envelopes them. When they awaken, the memory of their ecstasy lingers and is communicated in the wordless exchange of affectionate glances and gestures. What casual affair can provide this? What loveless lust can bestow this to any man or woman? This realization that no place else will they find what they have in each other is what best protects them from the pitfalls of the middle years. And they know that what they have, they worked for. It did not come as a doorprize, the luck of the draw. It came as the result of effort; deliberate, often awkward and fumbling, often painful, but deliberate; and knowing this, they appreciate that only in this way could they have achieved what they did. Being thus, they see the emptiness in the lives of those who have not made the effort and they have no need for their company.

Thus far in our discussion of the middle years, we have described some characteristics of the relationship this couple has with their children and with each other.   Now let us examine a much more elusive phenomenon: *the individual's relationship with himself*.

The very matters which harass and vex most people in these years also concern the mature man and woman, but where others turn away to take refuge in "escapes" and empty rationalisms, they face them quite deliberately, if often unobtrusively.   This is no time for pleasant sermonizing nor comfortable philosophizing before the fire.   Every man and woman has unguarded moments when alone they face the mystery-shrouded questions of their very existence.   No thinking man has lived who has not questioned his roles, his goals, his beliefs — in short, the meanings of all he is and does. The fact that many cannot face the questions or pretend satisfaction with easy platitudes does not mean that those who do not turn away arrive at answers completely satisfying.   What the mature man does is take satisfaction in the very fact of facing the questions and being able to do so despite his awareness of his limitations.   He is not content with specious, hand-me-down answers; he relishes the right to seek his own, wherever the search may lead and however much he may err in his conclusions.   It is precisely this affirmation of his personal existence and his honest pursuit of his own beliefs that is the hallmark of his individual self.   In this, there is no arrogance and if he is not completely content to take the word of others, neither is he disrespectful thereof, because he knows he could be wrong.   For some, it leads to a break with traditional modes of thought and of faith.   For others, it may lead back to an orthodoxy once abandoned. Wherever it goes, his satisfaction derives from his making a personal choice.

Related to this is a more practical consideration. Just as this individual crystallizes his philosophic outlook, he also makes provisions for his way of life in the years to come. Most people attempt to provide for the later years of life through savings, insurance, pension plans and other economic devices. This is understandable, but what many fail to do is save for what some call a "mental rainy day." This means to have attitudes, values, beliefs and interests which will be useful and available when the pattern of daily life must necessarily alter by reason of changes in the family group, job and advancing age. Increased leisure time is a curse for those unprepared for it. How many men and women, once the children are married and work lightened, wander the corridors of time in wretchedness, grasping for pleasures, fearful of the future?

In the middle years, the mature individual cultivates interests, often by trial and error. His curiosity remains high and he explores the world in search of new sources of satisfaction to which he will some day be able to give more time. It matters little what one undertakes as long as it can fulfill our needs by yielding intellectual and emotional satisfaction. For some it may be gardening or woodwork. Others find new pleasures in music, even learning to play an instrument. Some pursue courses of study in fields remote from their daily work. Some become involved in special community groups such as clubs for young people, hospital and church work. In whatever undertaking they choose, they re-experience some of the excitement of discovery they knew as children, but now with the advantage of age and experience to guide them, they can better see the possibilities and depths of their pursuits. As their interests materialize they realize they would like to devote more time to them, but cannot because of other obligations and it is at this point that important attitudes are crystallized. The "future" is seen as a time when such indulgences are more available and it is this looking forward to the time when, having worked for it, we are now privileged to do the things we have long anticipated that makes the future attractive. I am reminded of an incidental episode in Kazantzakis' novel "Zorba the Greek" in which a very old man is planting a young tree. When asked why he was doing this, with little likelihood of living long enough to see the tree bear fruit, the old man said, "I live each day as if I am going to live forever." Thus it is with all mature people — they live for the future, sensing the prerogatives and privileges of each decade and able to give up those of the past for those of the present and the future.

In diversifying our interests and involving ourselves with many things we avoid the dangerous business of putting all our emotional eggs in one basket. However deeply one loves one's mate or children, there must be room for other significant values. This is not merely to protect one's self against a tragic loss through sickness or accident, though that is a factor to be reckoned with, but beyond that we must see that we love and are loved for what we are as total personalities. The man or woman with creative hobbies and interests is more respected, admired and loved because of these things which make them more interesting personalities to be and live with. Love is not enough, and mature love leaves room for the continuous growth of the personality through self-expression in many areas. Too often, elderly couples are bored with themselves and each other — they have nothing to do or to talk about. The possession of interests and associates of like mind keeps us young in spirit though the body may age. In the middle years we prepare for that.

The use of what leisure time we do have deserves careful consideration. It is more than a matter of each individual deciding what would be fun for themselves without regard for other members of the family. This requires some planning and some compromises which may not be very easy to make. Children are usually delighted by the participation of parents in some of their play. This is especially true in the evenings, when the hour or so before bedtime can allow the family group to feel close and secure in their shared activities. Reading aloud while the kids have milk and cookies can be a wonderful experience for all. Games of a quiet nature are also useful. At times, there will be homework to do and parents can be helpful by their interest in the subjects and their assistance. An attitude toward learning can be encouraged by the enthusiasm of the parents in coaching and leading the youngsters to find pleasure in "looking things up" and discussing topics from school. For the parent, there is reward in the simple fact of being instrumental in the intellectual growth of a child.

Too many dads are ill-at-ease with very young boys, and wait for the day when as pals they can go fishing or hunting or golfing together. For the first ten years or so they are apt to leave it to mother to "play" with junior. Then, too late, they find out that junior is not much interested in playing with Dad. The mature man gives of his leisure time early in the life of the child and leads him into and through the variety of shared recreational activities. All this may take no more than a few half-hours a week, but it is enough to make contact in an important area of experience.

Parents, too, should have the ability to play together at home. The TV set can be a threat to this phase of their life. It matters little if it is casino, scrabble, chess or working a jig-saw puzzle, just so it is relaxing and entertaining. It is good for children to observe this — to see that parents do play games and recognize that keenness of competition need not involve arguments and bickering. And should the children observe that the winner collects a kiss from the loser, they cannot but feel that all's well with the world they live in.

The middle years, then, represent a period during which we live more for the familiar than with the new. Things have become fairly routine and most people have become more or less set in their ways. Job and home, family and friends, all have acquired some measure of the commonplace, yet this in itself is, as we have tried to point out, not without its own dangers. As in so many things, to be forewarned is to be forearmed, and maturity of attitude can alert us to the pitfalls of this time of life; when through deliberate self-examination and deliberate action we can again find the means to a more satisfying way of life. For each couple the "program" will differ in specific items, but the successful couple will have worked theirs out together.

6. *The Later Years*

From what has preceded this chapter we can pretty well guess the general quality and pattern of adjustment likely to be demonstrated by mature couples in the so-called later years of marriage. However, there are some specific situations which merit our attention.

First, the relationship with children and grand-children. Because of their own broad interests and overall perspectives, they do not attach themselves exclusively to their offspring. They can maintain a "hands-off" policy in the personal affairs of their children without sacrificing their sincere interests and concern. They do not demand regularly scheduled visits or calls, nor feel hurt and unwanted if some time passes without such. On the other hand, they do not permit themselves to be made into glorified baby-sitters nor arbitrators in every minor skirmish of the young couple. They respect the privacy of their children and want the same in return.

Too many older parents make a great issue of the necessity to feel "wanted" and useful, but unwittingly mean being catered to and made the central figure in the lives of their children. They expect and demand attentions and services in a manner to irritate and yet arouse guilt feelings in others, creating an atmosphere of tension in the relationship which leaves all parties strained and dissatisfied. The Biblical injunction "to honor thy father and thy mother . . ." is a very proper

one, but demands some interpretation.   It is unfort-
unate that some parents see only the law and not the
implications as regard their own roles.   Honor and
respect are rendered when people inspire it.   Tribute
may be given to a tyrant, but not love.   There are
moral obligations we all have toward parents and these
cannot be delegated properly to anyone else, but
anything beyond that will be a product of the personalities of all parties concerned.   Let us face the fact
that not all elderly married people are equally lovable
nor good and that many a marriage has been spoiled
by domineering, demanding or passively-aggressive
partners who, leech-like, drain the very substance of
the relationship from the hearts of their children.

The mature parents do not "need" their children
in the same way others do.   They are busy with their
own affairs and need not gain their emotional satisfactions through control of their children.   For them it
is enough that they see their children successfully
managing their own lives in an increasingly mature
manner.   They do not feel the children "owe" them
anything — if there is a debt at all, payment must be
made to the succeeding generation — the precious gift
was created to be handed down.   If what we have
given is indeed precious, our reward will be in kind,
even as it passes from our hands to theirs and to their
children's children; for this, too, is a labor of love.

Secondly, in their relationship with each other, the
elderly couple will make capital of their early efforts
and achieve a companionship that is mutually support-
ing and endearing.   Accepting their limitations, they
find new depths in simple pleasures shared and they

welcome time and opportunity for just being together. The hobbies and interests cultivated earlier now become sources of creative experience which fill the days of their lives and provide not only emotional outlets directly, but subjects for discussion between themselves and their friends. It has been said that a child's play is adult's work — that is, children in their play imitate adults at their work. In the later years, adults can play, in the same emotional sense that children do, but with the added pleasure of satisfaction deriving from their mature, experienced grasp of meanings and values. What is new and exciting to a child can be experienced by an adult, but for the latter there is the additional thrill of fitting it into an established background of experience — as if a goal long sought had at last been grasped.

Thirdly, and on a more sombre, but none-the-less optimistic note, we must accept the inevitability of death; not alone the prospect of our own, but that of mates and old friends. The mature person is far better protected from the ravages of grief than the lesser person. It may seem paradoxical that where one has loved so deeply and intensely, the grief reaction should be less, yet this is the case. This is true for several reasons: (1) there is less unconscious guilt toward the deceased — the immature person often harboring deeply buried resentments and death-wishes against the mate, which come out in the form of extravagant and violent protestations of grief; (2) the very nature of their love involved an acceptance of life *and* death, enabling them to be grateful for what they had rather than embittered over their loss; and (3) they still have emotional investments in life to which they can turn, confident that in so doing they are doing that of which the deceased would approve. For the mature personality, life is for living and he drinks deeply from its cup. If it must contain the bitter as well as the sweet, so be it, for this is in the nature of things. And also in the nature of things is the simple truth which has been a thesis of this book, that happiness is a thing called love.

CHAPTER IV

A NOTE OF REASSURANCE

It is altogether probable that among those who read this book, there will be some who will be disturbed by what they have read. I am concerned for those who may experience some degree of irritation and perhaps even some measure of anxiety in response to various aspects of what I may have quite strongly expressed. Some may feel I have described contemporary life so harshly that, if conditions are actually as I have depicted them, there is no hope for us, collectively. Others may feel that my criteria for maturity and my standards of success in marriage are so lofty that there is no hope for us individually. Many may be disturbed because they regard themselves as intelligent mature people, leading normal lives, yet find their ways to be quite different from that which I have described as ideal in Chapter III. Whatever the feelings and specific reasons may be, let me at this time add a note of reassurance.

If I have described contemporary life in too harshly critical terms, I have drawn no worse a picture than has been done by many others. But I also number myself among those who remain confident that despite these conditions all of us possess resources within ourselves which can be utilized to find a more satisfying way of life. I have tried to indicate the nature of some of these resources and how through deliberate effort we can alter our relationships with others and perhaps slowly shift the tide of battle against the destructive forces which threaten us.

If I have set up standards for a successful marriage based on a concept of maturity that seems beyond our capacity to achieve, I would remind us that there are no perfect individuals and no perfect marriages. On the other hand, we have always had our heroes and heroines; our ego-ideals whose qualities we have wished to incorporate and whom we have imitated to one degree or another. Beyond human models, we have also had our personal ideals as represented in a variety of ethico-religious systems. Much of religion is concerned with the way we live and the way in which we ought to live, and usually, though these are somewhat beyond our individual abilities to imitate very successfully, we accept them as guides and models. If I have set up an ideal that seems beyond reach, it is with no intention of discouraging anyone as to his own capabilities, but rather to establish a meaningful model to guide us in our pursuit of happiness. None of us do a perfect job. None of us who are willing to be honest with ourselves can avoid having anxious moments of doubt and despair. This need not be a cause for abandonment of hope. It could be the beginning of real growth and change, if we are but willing to do something about it.

At any time in a marriage, all of us are frequently shocked by thoughts and feelings which creep into our thinking; thoughts of hate and violence toward those we are supposed to love, desires for prohibited sexual experiences, harsh feelings toward our children, and others equally unacceptable. At times we have

all acted in ways we regret or for which we have made
weak excuses. This is true of the mature person and
the immature. It can and does happen in very successful marriages. The difference lies in the frequency,
consistency *and* what the individual does about it.
The less mature person is apt to content himself with
the observation, "I know I am not perfect — I have
my faults," and let it rest there. The more mature
person will face these feelings and actions and seek to
do something about them. They will not be allowed
to enlarge and become the basis of a serious division
between them and their families.

The long road to maturity is marked by difficulties
for all of us and we should judge ourselves not by the
presence or absence of problems, but by what we do
about them. If we feel anxiety, doubt and resentment, let us accept these as signals to which there are
appropriate responses to be made. Just as pain or
cough alerts us to the presence of physical disorders,
so, too, our more complex emotional reactions may call
our attention to the presence of problems of personal
adjustment. In the case of pain or cough, we usually
first try familiar home-remedies and if these do not
work we call in our family doctor. If he cannot handle
the case alone, he may in turn call in the specialist.
All of this is regarded as quite proper. So, too, it can
be with emotional problems. I have attempted to
indicate what we might all *wish* to be and achieve.
If we have too many psychic aches and pains in the
process, we can often call upon trusted friends for
frank advice or opinion on our behavior or we may
wish the counseling and guidance of a lawyer or clergy-
man whose position and reputation we respect. If this

does not suffice, we may then seek the aid of the specialist trained to deal with problems of human adjustment. He may work with us individually, or with both members of the marital partnership, or even recommend participation in a group of married people who, under a skilled leader, work out common problems. As long as we are willing to change, there are resources within ourselves and each other for such; in an atmosphere of mutual respect and where there is understanding. There is nothing that is in any of us that cannot stand the clear light of honest examination and in all of us are the varied faults as well as strengths, the foolishness and the wisdom, the dross and the gold that mixed together distinguish us as human beings.

Finally, I would wish to reassure those who might feel that the author has openly or insidiously attacked any institutionalized beliefs, be they sacred or secular. If there were in our life and times but one religious faith, subscribed to by all peoples, and but one system of scientific theory, and that one quite in harmony with the existing faith, then this present work might possibly be evaluated in terms of its harmony or dissonance with the prevailing beliefs. The world does not rest easy in the comfortable security of a single social philosophy, religious faith or universal scientific theory. From the time of primitive man and from the days of our own infancy, driven by wonder, curiosity and fear, we have struggled to explain ourselves and our world and to make life meaningful and secure. We have many religions, many social philosophies and many scientific theories, attesting to the fact of the struggle and the inconclusiveness of our knowledge.

Yet we continue the search. Knowledge increases and all things change under the impact thereof, however enduring some things seem to be. For the author, whatever we may become as individuals, whatever we may aspire to be, will derive from the nature of what we have been and are as human organisms. If this places our feet on a materialistic ground, it need not prohibit us from reaching for the stars. If the biologist and the psychiatrist insist they have a contribution to make toward a better understanding of man, we are not so arrogant as to believe that we alone possess the truth. We do believe that with learning comes change. New information permits a wider range of choices of behavioral responses, and if our choices are limited by the nature of what we are and the extent of our knowledge, at least we are relatively free to make them. I believe that in man's capacity to learn and to love lies mankind's best hope, and that only in the studied pursuit thereof can he realize his own best potentials. It is in the fullness of mature love that most of us have our greatest chance for happiness and no man or woman willing to work for it can fail to gain something from the effort; for the privilege and the joy lies not only in the reward, but in the task, itself. None of us are so mature but what we can, with effort, become better than we have been in our adjustment to love, sex and marriage.

BIBLIOGRAPHY

The references listed below comprise but a very small portion of a really enormous number of books which are pertinent to the subject of marriage. I have tried to select a few which might be regarded as representative sources to which the reader may wish to turn for further study.

RECOMMENDED READINGS

1. *The Direction of Human Development.* Montagu, M. F. A., Harper & Bros., New York, 1955

2. *Primitive Heritage.* Mead, M. and Calas, M., Random House, New York, 1953

3. *Childhood and Society.* Erickson, E. H., Norton & Co., New York, 1950

4. *Personality.* Murphy, G., Harper & Bros., New York, 1947

5. *Symbolic Wounds.* Bettelheim, B., The Free Press, Glencoe, Ill., 1954

6. *The Ethics of Sexual Acts.* Guyon, R., Knopf, Inc., New York, 1948

7. *Sex and the Nature of Things.* Berrill, N. J., Dodd, Mead & Co., New York, 1954

8. *Male and Female.* Mead, M., Morrow & Co., New York, 1949

9. *Patterns of Sexual Behavior.* Ford, C. S. and Glach, F. A., Harper & Bros., New York, 1951

10. *Psychology of Women.* (Vols. I and II) Deutsch, H., Grune and Stratton, New York, 1945

11. *Modern Woman: The Lost Sex.* Lundberg, G. and Farnham, M. F., Harper & Bros., New York, 1947

12. *Emotional Problems of Living.* English, O. S. and Pearson, G., Norton & Co., New York, 1945

13. *Psychoanalysis.* Thompson, Clara, Heritage House, Inc., New York, 1950

14. *Fundamentals of Psychoanalysis.* Alexander, F., Norton & Co., Inc., New York, 1948

15. *Successful Marriage.* Fishbein, M., and Burgess, E. W., Doubleday and Co., Inc., New York, 1948

16. *Marriage for Moderns.* Bowman, Henry A., Whittlesey House, New York, 1942

17. *Sex, Marriage and Family.* Rice, T. B., Lippincott, Philadelphia, 1946

18. *Man Against Myth.* Dunham, B., Little, Brown & Co., Boston, 1947

19. *The Impact of Science on Society.* Russell, B., Simon & Schuster, New York, 1953

20. *Human Destiny.* Du Nouy, L., Longmans, Green & Co., Inc., London, 1947

21. *Becoming.* Allport, G. W., Yale Univ. Press, New Haven, 1955

22. *The Art of Loving.* Erich Fromm, Harper & Bros., New York, 1956

23. *Love in the Western World.* Dennis De Rougemont, Pantheon Books, Inc., New York, 1956